CW00405505

10
minute

Maths
Assessments

for ages 5-6

CONTENTS

Assessment for learning

It is widely acknowledged that effective learning takes place where teachers understand their pupils' standards of achievement and lead the pupils forwards from these standards.

> *Assessment for learning is the process of seeking and interpreting evidence for use by learners and their teachers to decide where the learners are in their learning, where they need to go and how best to get there.*
>
> (Assessment for Learning: 10 principles – Assessment Reform Group)

This book will help you to assess your pupils' progress by providing activities that are quick and easy to administer, that can be used on a regular basis and that will help you build a profile of each pupil's attainment. Each activity will provide you with evidence of achievement that you can use for on-going pupil assessment and will help you focus your teaching and planning on the specific learning requirements of each child in your class.

Using the materials in this book will provide opportunities for both formative and summative assessment. It is recommended that the activities are used on a regular basis as part of an ordinary maths lesson, for continuous formative assessment. Recording the progress of each pupil, using the recording grid provided, will also assist you in making regular summative assessments in relation to National Curriculum levels of attainment.

All aspects of the *Framework for mathematics* for Year 1 are addressed through the assessment of separate learning objectives. These learning objectives are drawn from Strands 2 to 7 of the Framework:

2. Counting and understanding number
3. Knowing and using number facts
4. Calculating
5. Understanding shape
6. Measuring
7. Handling data

Many of the activities can also be used to support your assessment of Strand 1 (*Using and applying mathematics*). The teachers' notes accompanying each activity indicate where an assessment is particularly relevant to this.

How to use the activities for assessing pupils' progress

Ideally, pupils will work with an adult on an individual basis or in a very small group to enable the adult to make effective judgements about each individual's achievement. Everything achieved by the pupil should be a learning experience, perhaps where a particular skill or an aspect of knowledge is being strengthened and consolidated, or where a style of layout or method is being encountered for the first time. However, the assessment activities should only be used when the pupil has some prior experience of the work being assessed.

A pupil may be able to complete some, but not all, of the learning objectives. Any adult working closely with a pupil may discover 'gaps' in their understanding that can be reported back to the class teacher for monitoring and planning purposes. Further practice, focusing on specific areas, will help to fill these gaps and the assessment can then be repeated when the pupil is ready.

What's on the CD

The CD that accompanies this book can be used on a computer or CD player and features an audio track that can be used for the assessments that require audio. Children are often more focused when listening to a recording as the sound of a different voice helps to hold their attention. The teachers' notes for each assessment indicate whether there is an accompanying audio track and its number on the CD.

The CD also includes a recording grid on which you can indicate whether individual children have achieved specific learning objectives. You may decide not to use all the assessments with every pupil. In some cases, you might feel that you already have sufficient evidence that a child has achieved the specific objective and so leave it out. You may also decide to complete the assessments in a different order from the order in this book.

By filling in the the recording grid you will be able to build a clear picture of an individual's strengths and weaknesses as well as the class as a whole. The recording grid can be used to form an evidence base for assessing the National Curriculum level of each pupil, i.e. summative assessment. Your school or local authority will provide guidance regarding interpretation of evidence to make decisions about pupils' levels. Each pupil will be deemed to have reached a 'low', 'secure' or 'high' standard against the level criteria. Our recording grid uses these 'standards' (with red for 'low', orange for 'secure' and green for 'high') in relation to each 'I can' statement to help you make appropriate decisions about the progress of each pupil and how you might focus your teaching on each pupil's learning requirements.

Note that assessments are **not** provided for the following statements from the *Framework for mathematics* as these can be adequately covered in day-to-day experiences:

- Visualise and use everyday language to describe the position of objects and direction and distance when moving them, for example when placing or moving objects on a board game

- Estimate, measure, weigh and compare objects, choosing and using suitable uniform non-standard or standard units and measuring instruments (e.g. a lever balance, metre stick or measuring jug)

Count reliably at least 20 objects

Count reliably at least 20 objects (estimate and check numbers of objects)

Building on previous learning

Before starting this unit check that the children can already:
- match sets of objects to numerals that represent the number of objects.
- say and use number names in order in familiar contexts.
- know that numbers identify how many objects are in a set.
- count reliably up to 10 everyday objects.
- estimate how many objects they can see and check by counting.
- count aloud in ones.
- recognise numerals 1 to 9.

Learning objectives

Assessment sheet 1 can be used for assessing two different learning objectives, the second of which involves a higher order skill. It is up to the adult working with the individual to decide whether the child has achieved both objectives.

Objective 1: Count reliably at least 20 objects, recognising that when rearranged the number of objects stays the same.

Objective 2: Estimate a number of objects that can be checked by counting.

Learning outcomes

The children will be able to:
- count reliably at least 20 real objects.
- count reliably at least 20 illustrated objects.
- estimate a number of objects and check by counting.

Success criteria

The children have a **secure** level of attainment in relation to Objective 1 if the following questions can be answered with a 'yes'.

Can the children...
... count reliably 5 different numbers of objects e.g. 15 bricks, 20 straws, etc?
... know that the number of bricks, straws, etc remains the same even when jumbled up?
... count accurately the 21 birds on the top half of Assessment sheet 1?

The children have a **secure** level of attainment in relation to Objective 2 if the following questions can be answered with a 'yes'.

Can the children...
... estimate the number of objects to within a range of 3 either side of the actual number, then check the number of objects using 3 different sets of objects e.g. 9 counters, 10 pencils, etc?
... estimate the number of fish shown on the bottom half of Assessment sheet 1 to within a range of 3 either side of the actual number (11), then check by counting?

Administering the assessment

Ideally the children should work in a small group with an adult. Choose a quiet area to work and prepare several sets of objects e.g. bricks, counters, toy cars, straws, pencils, etc. Use these objects and the top half of Assessment sheet 1 to assess Objective 1. Use different numbers of the same objects and the bottom half of Assessment sheet 1 to assess Objective 2. Note that the pupils do not necessarily have to write down the answers — they could say them instead.

Counting reliably at least 20 objects

Name

Date

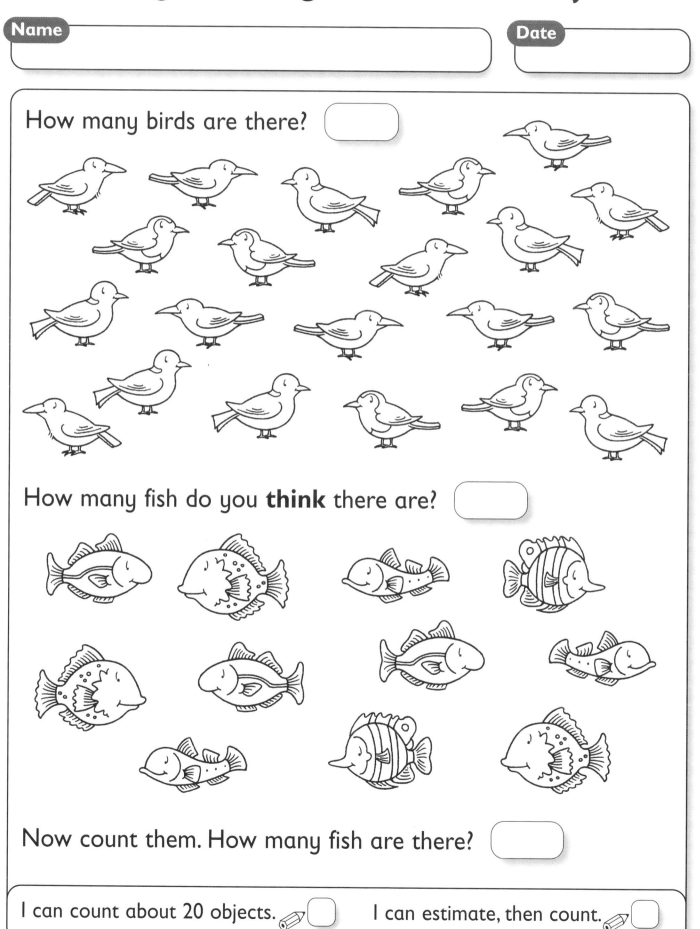

How many birds are there?

How many fish do you **think** there are?

Now count them. How many fish are there?

I can count about 20 objects. ✏️☐   I can estimate, then count. ✏️☐

Read and write numerals from 0 to 20

Building on previous learning

Before starting this unit check that the children can already:

- match sets of objects to numerals that represent the number of objects.
- say and use number names in order in familiar contexts.
- know that numbers identify how many objects are in a set.
- count reliably up to 10 everyday objects.
- estimate how many objects they can see and check by counting.
- count aloud in ones.
- recognise numerals 1 to 9.

Learning objectives

Assessment sheet 1 can be used for assessing two different learning objectives, the second of which involves a higher order skill. It is up to the adult working with the individual to decide whether the child has achieved both objectives.

Objective 1: Read numerals from 0 to 20.
Objective 2: Write numerals from 0 to 20.

Learning outcomes

The children will be able to:

- read all numerals from from 0 to 20.
- write all numerals from from 0 to 20.

Success criteria

The children have a **secure** level of attainment in relation to Objective 1 if the following question can be answered with a 'yes'.

Can the children…
… read the numbers shown on the top half of Assessment sheet 2?

The children have a **secure** level of attainment in relation to Objective 2 if the following question can be answered with a 'yes'.

Can the children…
… write the numbers, as they are dictated to them, on the bottom half of Assessment sheet 2?

Administering the assessment

To assess Objective 1, point to each number in turn and ask the children to tell you what each one says. They should be able to say the name of each number confidently and clearly. The CD can be used when assessing Objective 2. Children often work more consistently when listening to a recording as it holds their attention but you may prefer to dictate the numbers yourself. In either case, point clearly to the box in which the pupils should write each number.

● Track 1   This is the script for the CD if you decide to dictate the questions.

Listen very carefully. I am going to tell you some numbers.
Write each number in a separate box on the sheet.
Can you write 17?
Now write 14.
Now write 8.
Write 12 in the next box.
Now write 20.
Can you write 10 in the next box?
Write 13 in the next box.
Now write zero.
Now write 16.
The last one: write 19.

Andrew Brodie: Ten Minute Maths Assessments ages 5–6 © A&C Black 2009

Read and write numerals from 0 to 20

Name

Date

Can you **read** these numbers?

15   7   4   0   19

20   11   18   14

17   12

Listen carefully to the CD or your teacher. Can you **write** the numbers?

I can read numbers from 0 to 20.

I can write numbers from 0 to 20.

Read and write numerals beyond 20

Building on previous learning

Before starting this unit check that the children can already:

- match sets of objects to numerals that represent the number of objects.
- say and use number names in order in familiar contexts.
- know that numbers identify how many objects are in a set.
- count reliably at least 20 objects.
- estimate how many objects they can see and check by counting.
- count aloud in ones.
- read and write numerals from 0 to 20.

Learning objectives

Assessment sheet 1 can be used for assessing two different objectives. It is up to the adult working with the individual to decide whether the child has achieved both Objective 1 and Objective 2, which is a higher order skill.

Objective 1: Read numerals between 20 and 101.
Objective 2: Write numerals between 20 and 101.

Learning outcomes

The children will be able to:

- read any numerals between 20 and 100.
- write any numerals between 20 and 100.

Success criteria

The children have a **secure** level of attainment in relation to Objective 1 if the following question can be answered with a 'yes'.

Can the children…
… read the numbers shown in the upper part of Assessment sheet 3?

The children have a **secure** level of attainment in relation to Objective 2 if the following question can be answered with a 'yes'.

Can the children…
… write the numbers below as they are dictated to them in the boxes on the lower part of Assessment sheet 3?

Administering the assessment

To assess Objective 1, point to each number in turn and ask the children to tell you what each one says. They should be able to say the name of each number confidently and clearly. The CD can be used when assessing Objective 2. Children often work more consistently when listening to a recording as it holds their attention but you may prefer to dictate the numbers yourself. In either case, point clearly to the box in which the pupils should write each number.

Track 2   This is the script for the CD if you decide to dictate the questions.

Listen very carefully. I am going to tell you some numbers.
Write each number in a box on the sheet.
Can you write 21?
Now write 30.
In the next box write 37.
Now write 25.
Write 32 in the next box.
Now write 46.
Can you write 50 in the next box?
Now write 63.
Now write 78.
Can you write 99 in the last box?

Andrew Brodie: Ten Minute Maths Assessments ages 5–6 © A&C Black 2009

Read and write numerals beyond 20

Name

Date

Can you **read** these numbers?

23   36   100   83

48   94

27   65

51   72

Listen carefully to the CD or your teacher. Can you **write** these numbers?

I can read numbers from 20 to 100.

I can write numbers from 20 to 100.

Position numbers from 0 to 20 on a number line or track

Building on previous learning

Before starting this unit check that the children can already:
- say and use number names in order in familiar contexts.
- use language such as 'more' or 'less' to compare two numbers.
- read and write numerals from 0 to 20.

Learning objectives

Objective 1: Position numbers from 0 to 20 on a number line or number track.

Learning outcomes

The children will be able to:
- Position numbers from 0 to 20 correctly on a number line or number track.

Success criteria

The children have a **secure** level of attainment in relation to Objective 1 if the following questions can be answered with a 'yes'.

Can the children...
- ... position correctly any number from 0 to 20 on a number line?
- ... position correctly any number from 0 to 20 on a number track?

Administering the assessment

The children should already be familiar with number lines/tracks that appear regularly within maths lessons. However, this activity provides further practice of positioning numbers in the correct place as well as reading and writing the numbers correctly. It might also reveal unexpected misunderstandings and misconceptions.

◯ Track 3 The CD can be used for this assessment and has the advantage of focussing pupils' attention on the task. Some pupils will need help finding the diagrams referred to so you may need to point to each number line/track as it is introduced to the child. This is the script for the CD if you decide to dictate the questions.

*Look at your worksheet. Can you find the letter **a**? Next to letter **a** there is a number line. Some of the numbers are missing. Write the numbers in the boxes as I say them to you.*
Write number 8 in the correct place.
Write number 2 in the correct place.
Write number 5 in the correct place.

*Look at your worksheet. Can you find the letter **b**? Next to letter **b** there is a number track. Some of the numbers are missing. Write the numbers in the boxes as I say them to you.*
Write number 3.
Write number 10.
Write number 6.
Now write 4.
Now write 7.

*Now find the letter **c**. Next to the letter **c** there is **a** number line. Write the numbers in the boxes as I say them to you.*
First write 15 in the correct place.
Now write 7.
Now write 11.
Now write number 18.

*Can you find the letter **d**? Next to letter **d** there is a number track. Some of the numbers are missing. Write the numbers in the boxes as I say them to you.*
Write number 13.
Write number 2.
Write number 16.
Now write 9.

(Note that this assessment can be used to support your assessment of Using and applying mathematics: Describe simple patterns and relationships involving numbers or shapes; decide whether examples satisfy given conditions.)

Position numbers from 0 to 20 on a number line or track

Name

Date

Look at the number line.

a

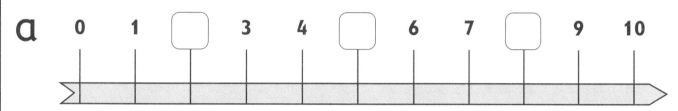

0   1   ☐   3   4   ☐   6   7   ☐   9   10

Look at the number track.

b 0 → 1 → 2 → ☐ → ☐ → 5 → ☐ → ☐ → 8 → 9 → ☐

Look at the number line.

c

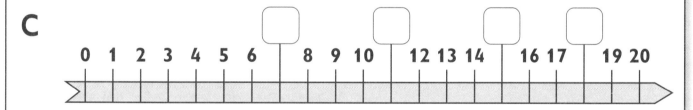

0 1 2 3 4 5 6 ☐ 8 9 10 ☐ 12 13 14 ☐ 16 17 ☐ 19 20

Look at the number track.

d 0 → 1 → ☐ → 3 → 4 → 5 → 6 → 7 → 8 → ☐ → 10

20 ← 19 ← 18 ← 17 ← ☐ ← 15 ← 14 ← ☐ ← 12 ← 11

I can write numbers in the correct place on a number line.

I can write numbers in the correct place on a number track.

Position numbers beyond 20 on a number line or track

Building on previous learning

Before starting this unit check that the children can already:
- say and use number names in order in familiar contexts.
- use language such as 'more' or 'less' to compare 2 numbers.
- read and write numerals from 0 to 20.
- read and write numerals beyond 20.

Learning objectives

Objective 1: Position numbers beyond 20 on a number line or track.

Learning outcomes

The children will be able to:
- position numbers beyond 20 on a number line or track.

Success criteria

The children have a **secure** level of attainment in relation to Objective 1 if the following question can be answered with a 'yes'.

Can the children…
… position correctly any number from 0 to 100 on a number line?

Administering the assessment

The children should already be familiar with number lines/tracks that appear regularly within maths lessons. However, this activity provides further practice of positioning numbers in correct places as well as reading and writing the numbers correctly. It might also reveal unexpected misunderstandings and misconceptions. This assessment uses a number line. Discuss the number line with the children before they start the assessment, ensuring they can follow the line from 0 to 100. If you feel that further practice is needed you could draw a number track and complete a similar assessment.

● Track 4   The CD can be used for this assessment and has the advantage of focussing pupils' attention on the task. This is the script for the CD if you decide to dictate the questions.

Look at the number line on your worksheet. Some of the numbers are missing. Write the numbers in the boxes as I say them to you.
Write number 68 in the correct place.
Write number 27 in the correct place.
Write number 52 in the correct place.
Now write number 39.
Write number 99.
Write number 43.
Now write number 75.

(Note that this assessment can be used to support your assessment of Using and applying mathematics: Describe simple patterns and relationships involving numbers or shapes; decide whether examples satisfy given conditions.)

Position numbers beyond 20 on a number line or track

Name

Date

Look at the number line.

0 1 2 3 4 **5** 6 7 8 9 **10** 11 12 13 14

☐ 26 **25** 24 23 22 21 **20** 19 18 17 16 **15**

28

30 31 32 33 34 **35** 36 37 38 ☐ **40** 41 42 ☐

29

57 56 **55** 54 53 ☐ 51 **50** 49 48 47 46 **45** 44

58

60 61 62 63 64 **65** 66 67 ☐ 69 **70** 71 72 73

59

87 86 **85** 84 83 82 81 **80** 79 78 77 ☐ 75 74

88

90 91 92 93 94 **95** 96 97 98 ☐ **100**

89

I can write numbers on a number line. ☐

Compare and order two numbers, using the related vocabulary

Building on previous learning

Before starting this unit check that the children can already:
- say and use number names in order in familiar contexts.
- use language such as 'more' or 'less' to compare two numbers.
- read and write numerals from 0 to 20.

Learning objectives

Objective 1: Compare two numbers using vocabulary such as 'more, bigger, greater, less, smaller, most'.

Learning outcomes

The children will be able to:
- compare numbers to others using the terms 'more' or 'less'.
- compare two numbers or amounts using the terms 'more, bigger, smaller, greater, larger, fewer'.

Success criteria

The children have a **secure** level of attainment in relation to Objective 1 if they can correctly identify the numbers referred to on the Assessment sheet.

Administering the assessment

The children should already be familiar with the vocabulary from their day-to-day experiences. However, for some children the variety of terms used may be confusing and they may need to have further practice during a maths lesson, possibly on an individual basis.

● Track 5   The CD can be used for this assessment and has the advantage of focussing pupils' attention on the task. Some children will need guidance on where to look on the Assessment sheet. The children can reply verbally to any of the assessment questions as an alternative to drawing rings. They **should** reply verbally when answering the question for box **g**. This is the script for the CD if you decide to dictate the questions.

Look at box a. Draw a ring around the bigger number.
Look at box b. Draw a ring around the smaller number.
Look at box c. Draw a ring around the number that is greater than 10.
Look at box d. Draw a ring around the number that is less than 10.
Look at box e. Draw a ring around the number that is more than 10.
Look at box f. Draw a ring around the larger number.
Look at box g. Shannon has collected 7 apples. Mike has collected 6 apples. Which child has more apples? Which child has fewer apples?

(Note that this assessment can be used to support your assessment of Using and applying mathematics: Describe simple patterns and relationships involving numbers or shapes; decide whether examples satisfy given conditions.)

Compare and order two numbers

Name

Date

a **8**   **4**

b **9**   **12**

c **5**   **13**

d **6**   **16**

e **9**   **11**

e **5**   **6**

g

Shannon

Mike

I can compare two numbers.

Andrew Brodie: Ten Minute Maths Assessments ages 5–6 © A&C Black 2009

Compare and order numbers three or more numbers, using the related vocabulary

Building on previous learning

Before starting this unit check that the children can already:

- say and use number names in order in familiar contexts.
- read and write numerals from 0 to 20.
- compare 2 numbers using vocabulary such as more, bigger, greater, less, smaller, most.

Learning objectives

Objective 1: Compare 3 or more numbers using vocabulary such as most, biggest, largest, greatest, fewest, least, smallest.

Learning outcomes

The children will be able to:

- compare 3 or more numbers or amounts using the terms 'biggest, most, greatest, least, smallest, fewest'.

Success criteria

The children have a **secure** level of attainment in relation to Objective 1 if they can correctly identify the numbers referred to on the Assessment sheet.

Administering the assessment

The children should already be familiar with the vocabulary from their day-to-day experiences. However, for some children the variety of terms used may be confusing and they may need further practice as part of their maths lesson, possibly on an individual basis.

● Track 6   The CD can be used for this assessment and has the advantage of focussing pupils' attention on the task. Some children will need guidance on how to follow the sheet. The children can reply verbally to the assessment questions rather than ringing the answers. Note that task **f** involves the same answer twice, but as a result of different vocabulary. This is the script for the CD if you decide to dictate the questions.

Look at box a. Draw a ring around the biggest number.
Look at box b. Draw a ring around the smallest number.
Look at box c. Draw a ring around the largest number.
Look at box d. Draw a ring around the smallest number
Look at box e. Draw a ring around the greatest number.
Look at box f. Kelly has 3 bananas. Josh has 4 bananas. Milly has 6 bananas.
Who has the most bananas?
Who has the fewest bananas?
Who has the greatest number of bananas?
Who has the least number of bananas?

You could extend task **f**, as furhter practice in comparing 2 quantities, by asking questions such as: Who has more bananas than Josh? Who has fewer bananas than Josh?

(Note that this assessment can be used to support your assessment of Using and applying mathematics: Solve problems involving counting, adding, subtracting.)

Compare and order three or more numbers

Name

Date

a **7   9   6**

b **4   6   5**

c **3   10   12   8**

d **15   11   13   17**

e **14   20   16   18**

f

Kelly   Jorsh   Milly

I can compare three or more numbers.

ndrew Brodie: Ten Minute Maths Assessments ages 5–6 © A&C Black 2009

Say the number that is 1 more or 1 less than any given number

Building on previous learning

Before starting this unit check that the children can already:
- say and use number names in order in familiar contexts.
- use language such as 'more' or 'less' to compare 2 numbers.
- read and write numerals from 0 to 20, then beyond; use knowledge of place value to position these numbers on a number track and number line.
- compare and order numbers, using the related vocabulary.

Learning objectives

Objective 1: Say the number that is 1 more than any given number.
Objective 2: Say the number that is 1 less than any given number.

Learning outcomes

The children will be able to:
- say or write down the number that is 1 more than any given number.
- say or write down the number that is 1 less than any given number.

Success criteria

The children have a **secure** level of attainment in relation to Objective 1 if the following question can be answered with a 'yes'.

Can the children…
… say the number that is 1 more than 7, 12, 19, 15, 3, 8, 20, 16?

The children have a **secure** level of attainment in relation to Objective 2 if the following question can be answered with a 'yes'.

Can the children…
… say the number that is 1 less than 6, 18, 20, 3, 1, 9, 14, 11?

Administering the assessment

The children should already be familiar with number lines/tracks that appear regularly within maths lessons and for this assessment they should be allowed to refer to a number line/track if they need to. Note that the Framework for mathematics specifies that pupils have to say the number that is '1 more' or '1 less than any given number'. It does not say that they have to *write* the number down and accordingly written recording by the child on the Assessment sheet is optional.

🔘 Track 7 The CD can be used for this assessment and has the advantage of focussing pupils' attention on the task. Look at the numbers on your worksheet. This is the script for the CD if you decide to dictate the questions.

What number is 1 more than 7?
What number is 1 more than 12?
What number is 1 more than 19?
What number is 1 more than 15?
What number is 1 more than 3?
What number is 1 more than 8?
What number is 1 more than 20?
What number is 1 more than 16?
What number is 1 less than 6?
What number is 1 less than 18?
What number is 1 less than 20?
What number is 1 less than 3?
What number is 1 less than 1?
What number is 1 less than 9?
What number is 1 less than 14?
What number is 1 less than 11?

(Note that this assessment can be used to support your assessment of Using and applying mathematics: Describe simple patterns and relationships involving numbers or shapes; decide whether examples satisfy given conditions.)

Say the number that is 1 more or 1 less than any given number

Name

Date

7	1 more →	

6	1 less →	

12	1 more →	

18	1 less →	

19	1 more →	

20	1 less →	

15	1 more →	

3	1 less →	

3	1 more →	

1	1 less →	

8	1 more →	

9	1 less →	

20	1 more →	

14	1 less →	

16	1 more →	

11	1 less →	

I can say a number that is 1 more than another number.

I can say a number that is 1 less than another number.

Andrew Brodie: Ten Minute Maths Assessments ages 5–6 © A&C Black 2009

Say the number that is 10 more or 10 less than a multiple of 10

Building on previous learning

Before starting this unit check that the children can already:

* say and use number names in order in familiar contexts.
* use language such as 'more' or 'less' to compare two numbers.
* read and write numerals from 0 to 20, then beyond; use knowledge of place value to position these numbers on a number track and number line.
* compare and order numbers, using the related vocabulary.

Learning objectives

Objective 1: Say the number that is 10 more than any multiple of 10.

Objective 2: Say the number that is 10 less than any multiple of 10.

Learning outcomes

The children will be able to:

* say or write down the number that is 10 more than any multiple of 10.
* say or write down the number that is 10 less than any multiple of 10.

Success criteria

The children have a **secure** level of attainment in relation to Objective 1 if the following question can be answered with a 'yes'.

Can the children…
… say the number that is 10 more than 40, 70, 50, 10, 30, 60, 90, 20?

The children have a **secure** level of attainment in relation to Objective 2 if the following question can be answered with a 'yes'.

Can the children…
… say the number that is 10 less than 70, 100, 10, 50, 30, 80, 40, 60?

Administering the assessment

The children should already be familiar with number lines/tracks that appear regularly within maths lessons. They should be allowed to refer to a number line/track if they need to. The Framework for mathematics specifies that pupils have to *say* the number that is '10 more' or '10 less than any multiple of 10' – it does not say that they have to *write* it down and accordingly written recording by the child on the Assessment sheet is optional.

● **Track 8** The CD can be used for this assessment and has the advantage of focussing pupils' attention on the task. This is the script for the CD if you decide to dictate the questions.

Look at the numbers on your worksheet.
What number is 10 more than 40?
What number is 10 more than 70?
What number is 10 more than 50?
What number is 10 more than 10?
What number is 10 more than 30?
What number is 10 more than 60?
What number is 10 more than 90?
What number is 10 more than 20?
What number is 10 less than 70?
What number is 10 less than 100?
What number is 10 less than 10?
What number is 10 less than 50?
What number is 10 less than 30?
What number is 10 less than 80?
What number is 10 less than 40?
What number is 10 less than 60?

(Note that this assessment can be used to support your assessment of Using and applying mathematics: Describe simple patterns and relationships involving numbers or shapes; decide whether examples satisfy given conditions.)

Say the number that is 10 more or 10 less than a multiple of 10

Name _____

Date _____

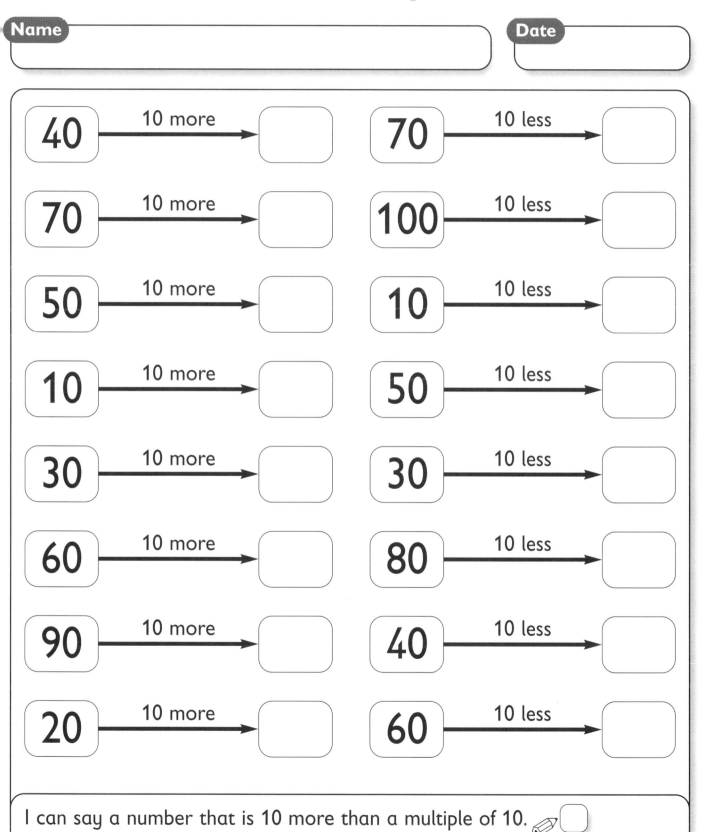

40	10 more → ☐		70	10 less → ☐	
70	10 more → ☐		100	10 less → ☐	
50	10 more → ☐		10	10 less → ☐	
10	10 more → ☐		50	10 less → ☐	
30	10 more → ☐		30	10 less → ☐	
60	10 more → ☐		80	10 less → ☐	
90	10 more → ☐		40	10 less → ☐	
20	10 more → ☐		60	10 less → ☐	

I can say a number that is 10 more than a multiple of 10. ✏ ☐

I can say a number that is 10 less than a multiple of 10. ✏ ☐

Andrew Brodie: Ten Minute Maths Assessments ages 5–6 © A&C Black 2009

Use the vocabulary of halves and quarters in context

Building on previous learning

Before starting this unit check that the children can already:

- use language such as 'circle' or 'bigger' to describe the shape and size of solids and flat shapes.

Learning objectives

Objective 1: Use the vocabulary of halves in context.
Objective 2: Use the vocabulary of quarters in context.

Learning outcomes

The children will be able to use the vocabulary of:

- halves when discussing food items such as cakes, pizzas, apples, bars of chocolate, etc.
- quarters when discussing food items such as cakes, pizzas, apples, bars of chocolate, etc.
- halves when discussing 2-D shapes such as circles and squares.
- quarters when discussing 2-D shapes such as circles and squares.

Success criteria

The children have a **secure** level of attainment in relation to Objective 1 if the following questions can be answered with a 'yes'.

Can the children…

… discuss portions of pizzas, cakes, etc. using the term 'half' appropriately?
… colour or otherwise indicate half of the circle and half of the square as shown on the Assessment sheet?

The children have a **secure** level of attainment in relation to Objective 2 if the following questions can be answered with a 'yes'.

Can the children…

… discuss portions of pizzas, cakes, etc. using the term 'quarter' appropriately?
… colour or otherwise indicate quarter of the circle and quarter of the square as shown on the Assessment sheet?

Administering the assessment

Take the opportunity to discuss halves and quarters with the children using a food item such as an apple or a pizza. Can the children identify halves and quarters effectively?

● Track 9   The CD can be used with the Assessment sheet and has the advantage of focussing pupils' attention on the task. This is the script for the CD if you decide to dictate the questions.

Look at box a.
Colour half the circle.
Colour half the square.
Look at box b.
Colour one quarter of the circle.
Colour one quarter of the square.

(Note that this assessment can be used to support your assessment of Using and applying mathematics: Describe simple patterns and relationships involving numbers or shapes; decide whether examples satisfy given conditions.)

Use the vocabulary of halves and quarters in context

Name

Date

a

b

I can use the vocabulary of halves in context.

I can use the vocabulary of quarters in context.

Derive all pairs of numbers with a total of 10

Building on previous learning

Before starting this unit check that the children can already:

- count reliably at least 20 objects, recognising that when rearranged the number of objects stays the same.
- compare and order numbers, using the related vocabulary.
- read and write numerals from 0 to 10.
- select two groups of objects to make a given total of objects.

Learning objectives

Objective 1: Derive all pairs of numbers with a total of 10.
Objective 2: Use the vocabulary related to addition and symbols to describe and record addition number sentences.
Objective 3: Use the equals sign.

Learning outcomes

The children will be able to:

- derive all pairs of numbers with a total of 10.
- write addition number sentences using the add sign (+) and equals sign (=).

Success criteria

The children have a **secure** level of attainment in relation to Objective 1 if the following question can be answered with a 'yes'.

Can the children...
... use the pictures on the Assessment sheet to help work out the number pairs that total 10?

The children have a **secure** level of attainment in relation to Objectives 2 and 3 if the following question can be answered with a 'yes'.

Can the children...
... write the addition number sentences to represent the number pairs that total 10?

Administering the assessment

Discuss the pictures of cats at the top of the page. Ensure that the children can count the 8 cats and 2 cats and know that there are 10 cats altogether. Ask the children to count the birds so that they know there are 10 birds. Encourage the children to write a number sentence, i.e. $8 + 2 = 10$, so that they know what is required. Now encourage them to write as many addition sentences as possible. The possible sentences are:

$10 + 0 = 10$	$0 + 10 = 10$
$9 + 1 = 10$	$1 + 9 = 10$
$8 + 2 = 10$	$2 + 8 = 10$
$7 + 3 = 10$	$3 + 7 = 10$
$6 + 4 = 10$	$4 + 6 = 10$
$5 + 5 = 10$	

At this stage we would not expect the children to write out the sentences in a systematic way as shown above. However, if they do so they are displaying high levels of ability in relation to several aspects of Using and applying mathematics.

Derive all pairs of numbers with a total of 10

Name

Date

There are 10 cats altogether.   8 + 2 = 10

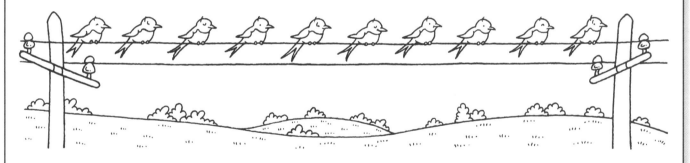

Write addition sentences for 10.

I can find pairs of numbers with a total of 10.

Andrew Brodie: Ten Minute Maths Assessments ages 5–6 © A&C Black 2009

Recall all pairs of numbers with a total of 10

Building on previous learning

Before starting this unit check that the children can already:

- count reliably at least 20 objects, recognising that when rearranged the number of objects stays the same.
- compare and order numbers, using the related vocabulary.
- read and write numerals from 0 to 10.
- select 2 groups of objects to make a given total of objects.

Learning objectives

Objective 1: Recall all pairs of numbers with a total of 10.
Objective 2: Use the vocabulary related to addition and symbols to describe and record addition number sentences.
Objective 3: Use the equals sign.

Learning outcomes

The children will be able to:

- recall all pairs of numbers with a total of 10.
- write addition number sentences using the add sign (+) and equals sign (=).

Success criteria

The children have a **secure** level of attainment in relation to Objective 1 if the following question can be answered with a 'yes'.

Can the children...
... answer confidently and quickly oral questions such as:
I have 6 balloons. How many more do I need to make 10 balloons?
I have 3 toy cars. How many more do I need to make a total of 10 toy cars?

The children have a **secure** level of attainment in relation to Objectives 2 and 3 if the following question can be answered with a 'yes'.

Can the children...
... write the addition number sentences to represent the number pairs that total 10?

Administering the assessment

🔘 Track 10   The CD can be used with the Assessment sheet and has the advantage of focussing pupils' attention on the task. You may like to go through the first question with the children, ensuring that they understand what is required. They do not need to draw pictures to complete each set to a total of 10, but can do so if they wish. However, the assessment concerns 'recall' of number facts and too much time spent drawing may not demonstrate this but may simply show that the children are able to 'derive' the facts, which is a skill of a lower order. This is the script for the CD if you decide to dictate the questions.

*I have 6 balloons. How many more do I need to make
10 balloons?*
Write the number sentence to show this.
*I have 3 toy cars. How many more do I need to make a total
of 10 toy cars?*
Write the number sentence to show this.
*I have 5 apples. How many more do I need to make a total
of 10 apples?*
Write the number sentence to show this.
*I have 8 marbles. How many more do I need to make a total
of 10 marbles?*
Write the number sentence to show this.

(Note that this assessment can be used to support your assessment of Using and applying mathematics:

- Describe simple patterns and relationships involving numbers or shapes; decide whether examples satisfy given conditions.
- Describe a puzzle or problem using numbers, practical materials and diagrams; use these to solve the problem and set the solution in the original context.
- Describe ways of solving puzzles and problems, explaining choices and decisions orally or using pictures.)

Recall all pairs of numbers with a total of 10

Name

Date

Listen carefully to the CD or your teacher.

I can find pairs of numbers with a total of 10.

Andrew Brodie: Ten Minute Maths Assessments ages 5–6 © A&C Black 2009

Work out subtractions from 10

Building on previous learning

Before starting this unit check that the children can already:
- count reliably at least 20 objects, recognising that when rearranged the number of objects stays the same.
- compare and order numbers, using the related vocabulary.
- read and write numerals from 0 to 10.
- derive and recall all pairs of numbers with a total of 10.

Learning objectives

Objective 1: Work out subtractions from 10.
Objective 2: Use the vocabulary related to subtraction and symbols to describe and record subtraction number sentences.
Objective 3: Use the equals sign.

Learning outcomes

The children will be able to:
- work out all subtractions from 10.
- record subtractions using subtraction number sentences containing the minus sign (–) and equals sign (=).

Success criteria

The children have a **secure** level of attainment in relation to Objective 1 if the following question can be answered with a 'yes'.

Can the children…
… use the pictures on the Assessment sheet to help work out the subtractions from 10?

The children have a **secure** level of attainment in relation to learning Objectives 2 and 3 if the following question can be answered with a 'yes'.

Can the children…
… write the subtraction number sentences to represent the subtractions from 10?

Administering the assessment

Provide the children with the Assessment sheet which shows 10 rabbits as a visual clue. The children can use these illustrations or concrete counting equipment such as counters, toy bears, etc. to help them to work out the answers to the questions shown. Once the children have completed these questions successfully, help them to write a subtraction sentence that has not already been used, before writing some on their own. The subtraction sentences possible are:

$10 - 9 = 1$
$10 - 2 = 8$
$10 - 7 = 3$
$10 - 4 = 6$
$10 - 5 = 5$
$10 - 0 = 10$

(Note that this assessment can be used to support your assessment of Using and applying mathematics: Describe simple patterns and relationships involving numbers or shapes; decide whether examples satisfy given conditions.)

Andrew Brodie: Ten Minute Maths Assessments ages 5–6 © A&C Black 2009

Work out subtractions from 10

Name

Date

Subtract from 10.

10 − 4 = ☐

10 − 8 = ☐

10 − 1 = ☐

10 − 6 = ☐

10 − 3 = ☐

10 − 10 = ☐

Write some subtraction sentences.

☐ ☐

☐ ☐

☐ ☐

I can work out subtractions from 10. ☐

I can write subtraction sentences. ☐

Andrew Brodie: Ten Minute Maths Assessments ages 5–6 © A&C Black 2009

Derive and recall addition facts for totals to at least 5

Building on previous learning

Before starting this unit check that the children can already:
- count reliably at least 20 objects, recognising that when rearranged the number of objects stays the same.
- compare and order numbers, using the related vocabulary.
- read and write numerals from 0 to 10.
- select 2 groups of objects to make a given total of objects.

Learning objectives

Objective 1: Derive and recall all pairs of numbers with a total of 3, 4 or 5.
Objective 2: Use the vocabulary related to addition and symbols to describe and record addition number sentences.
Objective 3: Use the equals sign.

Learning outcomes

The children will be able to:
- recall all pairs of numbers with a total of 3, 4 or 5.
- write addition number sentences using the add sign (+) and equals sign (=).

Success criteria

The children have a **secure** level of attainment in relation to Objective 1 if the following question can be answered with a 'yes'.

Can the children…
… answer confidently and quickly oral questions such as:

> I have 1 toy car. How many more do I need to make 3 toy cars?
> I have 1 counter. How many more do I need so that I have 4 counters?
> I have 3 bears. How many more do I need to make a total of 5 bears?

The children have a **secure** level of attainment in relation to Objectives 2 and 3 if the following question can be answered with a 'yes'.

Can the children…
… write the addition number sentences to represent the number pairs that total 3, 4 or 5?

Administering the assessment

Track 11 The CD can be used with the Assessment sheet and has the advantage of focussing pupils' attention on the task. You may like to go through the first question with the children, ensuring that they understand what is required. They do not need to draw pictures to complete each set to the totals specified, but can do so if they wish. However, the assessment concerns 'deriving' and 'recalling' the number facts and you may conclude that the drawing process simply shows that the children are able to 'derive' the facts, which is a skill of a lower order than the ability to 'recall' the facts. This is the script for the CD if you decide to dictate the questions.

I have 1 toy car. How many more do I need to make 3 toy cars?
Write the number sentence to show this.
I have 1 counter. How many more do I need so that I have 4 counters?
Write the number sentence to show this.
I have 3 bears. How many more do I need to make a total of 5 bears?
Write the number sentence to show this.

Once the children have completed the questions above, show them another way of making 5:

$$4 + 1 = 5.$$

Ask the children to show another way of making 3, another way of making 4 and another way of making 5. The possible alternatives to those already provided are:

$$2 + 1 = 3, \quad 0 + 3 = 3, \quad 3 + 0 = 3$$
$$2 + 2 = 4, \quad 3 + 1 = 4, \quad 4 + 0 = 4, \quad 0 + 4 = 4$$
$$5 + 0 = 5, \quad 0 + 5 = 5, \quad 1 + 4 = 5, \quad 2 + 3 = 5$$

Derive and recall addition facts for totals to at least 5

Name

Date

Listen carefully to the CD or your teacher.

I can find pairs of numbers with a total of 3.

I can find pairs of numbers with a total of 4.

I can find pairs of numbers with a total of 5.

Andrew Brodie: Ten Minute Maths Assessments ages 5–6 © A&C Black 2009

Work out subtraction facts for totals to at least 5

Building on previous learning

Before starting this unit check that the children can already:

- count reliably at least 20 objects, recognising that when rearranged the number of objects stays the same.
- compare and order numbers, using the related vocabulary.
- read and write numerals from 0 to 10.
- select 2 groups of objects to make a given total of objects.

Learning objectives

Objective 1: Work out the subtractions from totals to at least 5.

Objective 2: Use the vocabulary related to subtraction and symbols to describe and record subtraction number sentences.

Objective 3: Use the equals sign.

Learning outcomes

The children will be able to:

- work out all subtractions from 3, 4 and 5.
- record subtractions using subtraction number sentences containing the minus sign (−) and equals sign (=).

Success criteria

The children have a **secure** level of attainment in relation to Objective 1 if the following question can be answered with a 'yes'.

Can the children…
… use the pictures on the Assessment sheet to help work out the subtractions from 3, 4 and 5?

The children have a **secure** level of attainment in relation to learning Objectives 2 and 3 if the following question can be answered with a 'yes'.

Can the children…
… write the subtraction number sentences to represent the subtractions?

Administering the assessment

Provide the children with the Assessment sheet, which shows 3 bikes, 4 buses and 5 cars as visual clues. The children can use these illustrations or concrete counting equipment such as counters, toy houses, vehicles, etc. to help them to work out the answers. Once the children have completed the questions successfully, help them to write an extra subtraction sentence for 3, a subtraction sentence for 4 and a subtraction sentence for 5. The extra subtraction sentences possible are:

$$3 - 3 = 0 \quad 3 - 2 = 1 \quad 3 - 0 = 3$$
$$4 - 4 = 0 \quad 4 - 2 = 2 \quad 4 - 1 = 3 \quad 4 - 0 = 4$$
$$5 - 5 = 0 \quad 5 - 4 = 1 \quad 5 - 3 = 2 \quad 5 - 1 = 4 \quad 5 - 0 = 5$$

If you feel that the children are confident with these subtrations you may like to extend the activity to subtractions from higher numbers.

(Note that this assessment can be used to support your assessment of Using and applying mathematics: Describe simple patterns and relationships involving numbers or shapes; decide whether examples satisfy given conditions.)

Work out subtraction facts for totals to at least 5

Name

Date

Listen carefully to the CD or your teacher.

I can work out subtractions from 3.

I can work out subtractions from 4.

I can work out subtractions from 5.

Andrew Brodie: Ten Minute Maths Assessments ages 5–6 © A&C Black 2009

Count on or back in ones, twos, fives and derive multiples

Building on previous learning

Before starting this unit check that the children can already:

- count reliably at least 20 objects, recognising that when rearranged the number of objects stays the same.
- compare and order numbers, using the related vocabulary.
- read and write numerals from 0 to 20 then beyond; use knowledge of place value to position these numbers on a number track and number line.

Learning objectives

Objective 1: Count on or back in ones to 20.
Objective 2: Count on or back in twos to 20 and derive multiples.
Objective 3: Count on or back in fives to 50 and derive multiples.

Learning outcomes

The children will be able to:

- count on or back orally in ones to 20.
- count on in twos to 20, deriving multiples of 2 to the tenth multiple by recording on a number line, counting back in twos from 20 to 0.
- count on in fives to 50, deriving multiples of 5 to the tenth multiple by recording on a number line, counting back in fives from 50 to 0.

Success criteria

The children have a **secure** level of attainment in relation to Objective 1 if the following question can be answered with a 'yes'.

Can the children...
... count out loud in ones to 20, then count out loud from 20 to 0 in ones?

The children have a **secure** level of attainment in relation to Objective 2 if the following question can be answered with a 'yes'.

Can the children...
... count on in twos to 20, record the multiples of 2 on a number line, and count back in twos from 20 to 0?

The children have a **secure** level of attainment in relation to Objective 3 if the following question can be answered with a 'yes'.

Can the children...
... count on in fives to 50, record the multiples of 5 on a number line, and count back in fives from 50 to 0?

Administering the assessment

- Assess Objective 1 orally by asking the children to count up to 20. Once they have reached 20 ask them to count back to 0.
- For Objective 2 provide the children with the Assessment sheet, which shows a number line to 20 and ask the children to count in twos orally. If they are confident with this ask them to count in twos again, this time drawing rings around the numbers as they say them. Now ask them to count back from 20 in twos making use of the ringed numbers if necessary.
- For Objective 3 show the children the number line to 50 and ask them to count in fives orally. If they are confident with this ask them to count in fives again, this time drawing rings around the numbers as they say them. Now ask the children to count back from 50 in fives making use of the ringed numbers if necessary.

(Note that this assessment can be used to support your assessment of Using and applying mathematics: Describe simple patterns and relationships involving numbers or shapes; decide whether examples satisfy given conditions.)

Andrew Brodie: Ten Minute Maths Assessments ages 5–6 © A&C Black 200

Count on or back in ones, twos, fives and derive multiples

Name

Date

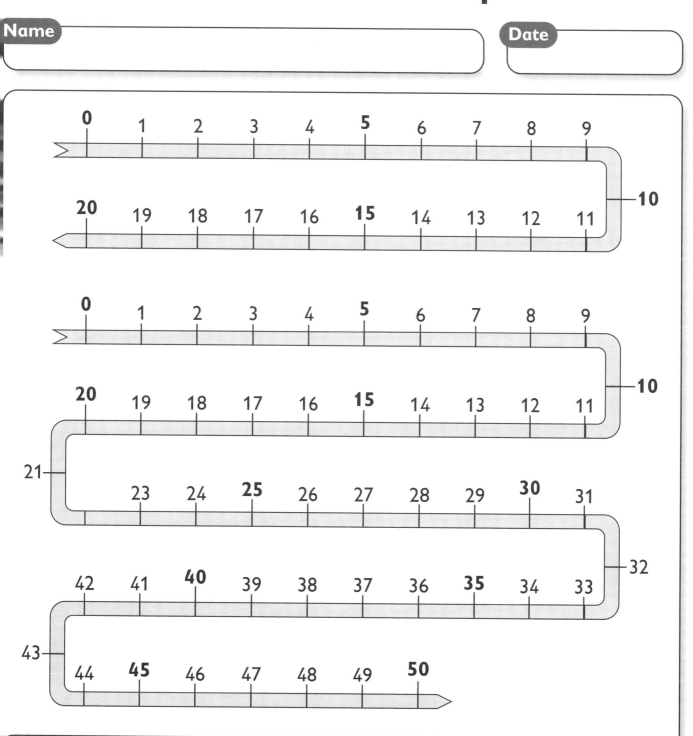

I can count on or back in ones.

I can count on or back in twos.

I can count on or back in fives.

ndrew Brodie: Ten Minute Maths Assessments ages 5–6 © A&C Black 2009

Count on or back in tens and derive multiples

Building on previous learning

Before starting this unit check that the children can already:

- count reliably at least 20 objects, recognising that when rearranged the number of objects stays the same.
- compare and order numbers, using the related vocabulary.
- read and write numerals from 0 to 20 then beyond; use knowledge of place value to position these numbers on a number track and number line.

Learning objectives

Objective 1: Count on or back in tens to 100 and derive multiples.

Learning outcomes

The children will be able to:

- count on in tens to 100, deriving multiples of 10 to the tenth multiple by recording on a number line, counting back in tens from 100 to 0.

Success criteria

The children have a **secure** level of attainment in relation to Objective 1 if the following question can be answered with a 'yes'.

Can the children...
... count on in tens to 100, record the multiples of 10 on a number line, and count back in tens from 100 to 0?

Administering the assessment

Provide the children with the Assessment sheet, which shows a number line to 100 and ask the children to count in tens orally. If they are confident with this ask them to count in tens again, this time drawing rings around the numbers as they say them. Now ask the children to count back from 100 in tens making use of the ringed numbers if necessary.

(Note that this assessment can be used to support your assessment of Using and applying mathematics: Describe simple patterns and relationships involving numbers or shapes; decide whether examples satisfy given conditions.)

Andrew Brodie: Ten Minute Maths Assessments ages 5–6 © A&C Black 200

Count on or back in tens and derive multiples

Name

Date

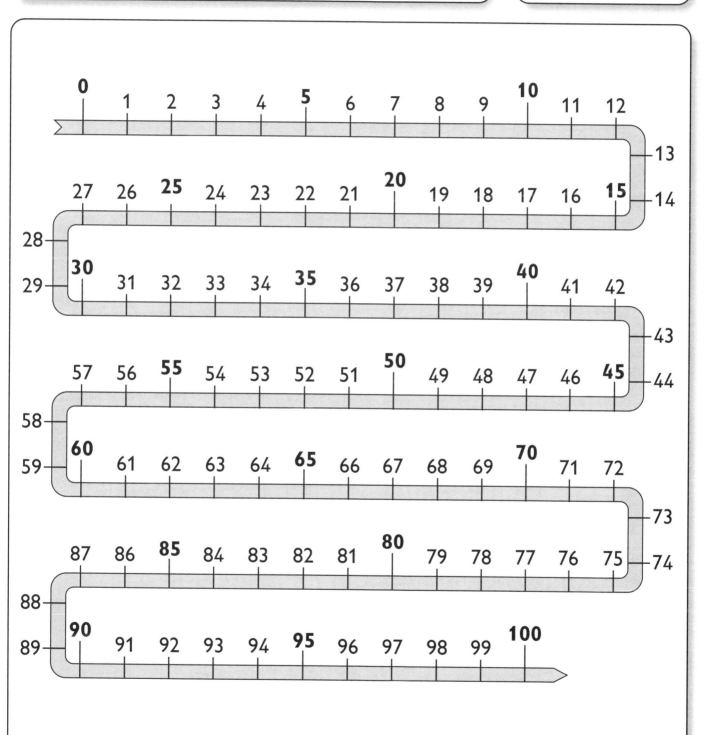

I can count on or back in tens.

Andrew Brodie: Ten Minute Maths Assessments ages 5–6 © A&C Black 2009

Recall the doubles of all numbers to at least 10

Building on previous learning

Before starting this unit check that the children can already:

- count reliably at least 20 objects, recognising that when rearranged the number of objects stays the same.
- compare and order numbers, using the related vocabulary.
- read and write numerals from 0 to 20 then beyond; use knowledge of place value to position these numbers on a number track and number line.

Learning objectives

Objective 1: Recall the doubles of all numbers to at least 10.

Objective 2: Solve problems involving counting, adding, subtracting, doubling or halving in the context of numbers, measures or money.

Learning outcomes

The children will be able to:

- recall the doubles of all numbers to at least 10.
- solve problems involving counting, adding and doubling in the context of numbers or money.

Success criteria

The children have a **secure** level of attainment in relation to Objective 1 if the following question can be answered with a 'yes'.

Can the children…
… recall the doubles of 7, 1, 4, 9, 3, 5, 2, 10, 6 and 8?

The children have a **secure** level of attainment in relation to Objective 2 if the following question can be answered with a 'yes'.

Can the children…
… find the doubles of 7 pence, and 4 pounds?

You may wish to make a judgement in relation to the whole of learning Objective 2 based on the performance of the child in this assessment exercise.

Administering the assessment

On this Assessment sheet the questions are numbered and it is essential that the children can distinguish between the question numbers and the numbers used within the questions. Show them the sheet and the numbering so that they understand exactly where to write the answers.

● Track 12 Although the questions are written on the sheet it is advisable to play the CD or dictate the questions below:

Question 1: What number is double 7?
Question 2: What number is double 1?
Question 3: What number is double 4?
Question 4: What number is double 9?
Question 5: What number is double 3?
Question 6: What number is double 5?
Question 7: What number is double 2?
Question 8: What number is double 10?
Question 9: What number is double 6?
Question 10: What number is double 8?
Question 11: Leela has 7 pence. Ben has double that amount. How much money does Ben have?
Question 12: Kamal has 4 pounds. Shannon has double that amount. How much money does Shannon have?

(Note that this assessment can be used to support your assessment of Using and applying mathematics: Describe simple patterns and relationships involving numbers or shapes; decide whether examples satisfy given conditions; Solve problems involving counting, adding, subtracting, doubling or halving in the context of numbers, measures or money.)

Recall the doubles of all numbers to at least 10

Name

Date

1. What number is double 7?

2. What number is double 1?

3. What number is double 4?

4. What number is double 9?

5. What number is double 3?

6. What number is double 5?

7. What number is double 2?

8. What number is double 10?

9. What number is double 6?

10. What number is double 8?

11. Leela has 7 pence. Ben has double that amount. How much money does Ben have?

12. Kamal has 4 pounds. Shannon has double that amount. How much money does Shannon have?

I can find doubles of numbers up to 10.

I can find doubles of amounts of money.

Relate addition to counting on
(Recognise that addition can be done in any order.)

Building on previous learning

Before starting this unit check that the children can already:

- count reliably at least 20 objects, recognising that when rearranged the number of objects stays the same.
- compare and order numbers, using the related vocabulary.
- read and write numerals from 0 to 20 then beyond; use knowledge of place value to position these numbers on a number track and number line.
- use the vocabulary related to addition and symbols to describe and record addition number sentences.

Learning objectives

Objective 1: Relate addition to counting on.
Objective 2: Recognise that addition can be done in any order.

Learning outcomes

The children will be able to:

- count on to find the total of 2 numbers.
- decide the order in which they wish to add the 2 numbers together.

Success criteria

The children have a **secure** level of attainment in relation to Objective 1 if the following question can be answered with a 'yes'.

Can the children…
… count on in ones to find the answers to the following questions:

5 + 2	12 + 3
6 + 3	18 + 6
8 + 4	15 + 7

The children have a **secure** level of attainment in relation to learning Objective 2 if the following question can be answered with a 'yes'.

Can the children…
… decide where to start when adding the 2 numbers in each of the following questions:

6 + 4	2 + 14
7 + 5	13 + 5
3 + 8	4 + 11

You will need to base your judgement on whether you feel that the children realise that it is more effective to start with the 6 and add on 4 in the first of these questions (and to follow this pattern in the second and fifth questions) but that it is easier to start with the 8 and add on 3 in the third question (and to follow this pattern with the fourth and sixth questions).

Administering the assessment

Provide the children with the Assessment sheet, which shows a number line to 25 and ask them to complete the questions shown on the sheet. Allow the children plenty of time to complete the questions and observe how they approach each one. Encourage the children to explain to you what they are doing.

(Note that this assessment can be used to support your assessment of Using and applying mathematics: Describe simple patterns and relationships involving numbers or shapes; decide whether examples satisfy given conditions.)

Relate addition to counting on

Name

Date

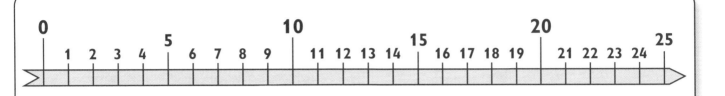

0 1 2 3 4 5 6 7 8 9 10 11 12 13 14 15 16 17 18 19 20 21 22 23 24 25

Answer these questions:

5 + 2 = ☐

6 + 3 = ☐

8 + 4 = ☐

12 + 3 = ☐

18 + 6 = ☐

15 + 7 = ☐

Now try these questions:

6 + 4 = ☐

7 + 5 = ☐

3 + 8 = ☐

2 + 14 = ☐

13 + 5 = ☐

4 + 11 = ☐

I can count on to find the answers to addition questions. ☐

I can decide which order to add the numbers together. ☐

Andrew Brodie: Ten Minute Maths Assessments ages 5–6 © A&C Black 2009

Use practical and informal written methods to support the addition of a one-digit number to a one-digit or two-digit number

Building on previous learning

Before starting this unit check that the children can already:

- count reliably at least 20 objects, recognising that when rearranged the number of objects stays the same.
- compare and order numbers, using the related vocabulary.
- read and write numerals from 0 to 20 then beyond; use knowledge of place value to position these numbers on a number track and number line.
- use the vocabulary related to addition and symbols to describe and record addition number sentences.

Learning objectives

Objective 1: Use practical and informal written methods to support the addition of a one-digit number to a one-digit or two-digit number.

Learning outcomes

The children will be able to:

- count on to find the total of 2 numbers.
- decide the order in which they wish to add the 2 numbers together.
- use practical equipment, such as counting apparatus in the form of counters, toys, etc.
- use number lines.

Success criteria

The children have a **secure** level of attainment in relation to Objective 1 if the following questions can be answered with a 'yes'.

Can the children…
… count on, deciding the order in which to add, to find the total in each of the following questions:
9 + 6   4 + 8   3 + 7?
… use counting equipment or number lines, together with informal written methods such as drawing the 'jumps' on the number lines, to find the answer to each of the following questions:
18 + 5   27 + 4   16 + 8   28 + 5
7 + 29   36 + 9?

Administering the assessment

Provide the children with Assessment sheet which shows a number line to 25 and ask them to complete the questions on the sheet. A variety of different counting equipment should also be available, together with some number lines and some blank sheets of paper so that the child can complete informal jottings and number line drawings. Allow the children plenty of time to complete the questions and observe how they approach each one. Encourage the children to explain to you what they are doing. At this stage there is not one 'correct' method. Providing each child's method is logical, s/he can achieve Objective 1, without having to use either the counting equipment or the number lines.

(Note that this assessment can be used to support your assessment of Using and applying mathematics: Describe simple patterns and relationships involving numbers or shapes; decide whether examples satisfy given conditions; Describe a puzzle or problem using numbers, practical materials and diagrams; use these to solve the problem and set the solution in the original context.)

Use practical and informal written methods to support addition

Name

Date

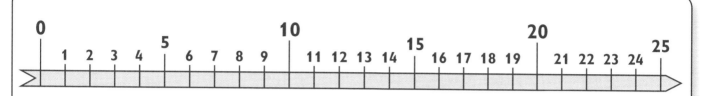

0 1 2 3 4 5 6 7 8 9 10 11 12 13 14 15 16 17 18 19 20 21 22 23 24 25

Answer these questions:

$9 + 6 =$ ⬜

$4 + 8 =$ ⬜

$3 + 7 =$ ⬜

$2 + 4 =$ ⬜

$5 + 1 =$ ⬜

$3 + 6 =$ ⬜

Now try these questions:

$18 + 5 =$ ⬜

$27 + 4 =$ ⬜

$16 + 8 =$ ⬜

$28 + 5 =$ ⬜

$7 + 29 =$ ⬜

$36 + 9 =$ ⬜

I can count on to find the answers to addition questions.

I can decide which order to add the numbers together.

I can use equipment or written methods to help me.

Andrew Brodie: Ten Minute Maths Assessments ages 5–6 © A&C Black 2009

Use practical and informal written methods to support the addition of a multiple of 10 to a one-digit or two-digit number

Building on previous learning

Before starting this unit check that the children can already:

- count reliably at least 20 objects, recognising that when rearranged the number of objects stays the same.
- compare and order numbers, using the related vocabulary.
- read and write numerals from 0 to 20 then beyond; use knowledge of place value to position these numbers on a number track and number line.
- use the vocabulary related to addition, and symbols to describe and record addition number sentences.
- count on or back in tens and derive the multiples of 10 to the tenth multiple.

Learning objectives

Objective 1: Use practical and informal written methods to support the addition of a multiple of 10 to a one-digit or two-digit number.

Learning outcomes

The children will be able to:

- count on to find the total of 2 numbers.
- decide the order in which they wish to add the 2 numbers together.
- use practical equipment, such as counting apparatus in the form of counters, toys, etc.
- use number lines.

Success criteria

The children have a **secure** level of attainment in relation to Objective 1 if the following questions can be answered with a 'yes'.

Can the children…
… count on, deciding the order in which to add, to find the total in each of the following questions?

| 30 + 6 | 4 + 50 | 60 + 7 |

… use counting equipment or number lines, together with informal written methods such as drawing the 'jumps' on the number lines, to find the answer to each of the following questions?

| 18 + 20 | 30 + 14 | 16 + 20 | 40 + 15 |
| 30 + 29 | 50 + 37 |

Administering the assessment

Provide the children with the Assessment sheet, which shows a number line to 100 and ask them to complete the questions. A variety of different counting equipment should also be available, together with some number lines and some blank sheets of paper for informal jottings or number line drawings. Allow the children plenty of time to complete the questions and observe how they approache each one. Encourage the children to explain to you what they are doing. At this stage there is not one 'correct' method. Providing each child's method is logical, s/he can achieve Objective 1, without having to use either the counting equipment or the number lines.

(Note that this assessment can be used to support your assessment of Using and applying mathematics: Describe simple patterns and relationships involving numbers or shapes; decide whether examples satisfy given conditions; Describe a puzzle or problem using numbers, practical materials and diagrams; use these to solve the problem and set the solution in the original context.)

Use practical and informal written methods to support the addition of a multiple of 10

Name

Date

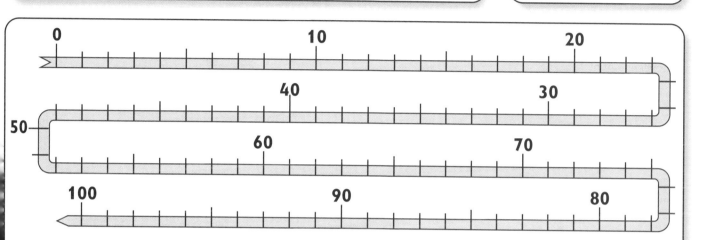

Answer these questions:

30 + 6 =

4 + 50 =

60 + 7 =

20 + 9 =

3 + 80 =

5 + 90 =

Now try these questions:

18 + 20 =

30 + 14 =

16 + 20 =

40 + 15 =

30 + 29 =

50 + 37 =

I can count on in tens to find the answers to addition questions.

I can decide which order to add the numbers together.

I can use equipment or written methods to help me.

Andrew Brodie: Ten Minute Maths Assessments ages 5–6 © A&C Black 2009

Understand subtraction (of a one-digit number) as take away

**Understanding subtraction as take away
(use practical and informal written methods to
support the subtraction of a one-digit number
from a one-digit or two-digit number)**

Building on previous learning

Before starting this unit check that the children can
already:

- count reliably at least 20 objects, recognising that when
  rearranged the number of objects stays the same.
- compare and order numbers, using the related
  vocabulary.
- read and write numerals from 0 to 20 then beyond; use
  knowledge of place value to position these numbers on a
  number track and number line.
- use the vocabulary related to subtraction and symbols
  to describe and record subtraction number sentences.

Learning objectives

Objective 1: Use practical and informal written methods
to support the subtraction of a one-digit number from a
one-digit or two-digit number

Learning outcomes

The children will be able to:

- 'take away' a number from a larger number.
- use practical equipment, such as counting apparatus in
  the form of counters, toys, etc.
- use number lines.

Success criteria

The children have a **secure** level of attainment in relation
to Objective 1 if the following questions can be answered
with a 'yes'.

Can the children…
… find the answers to the following questions, using a
process of taking away?

$9 - 4$	$7 - 3$	$8 - 5$
$6 - 1$	$9 - 7$	$5 - 0$

… use counting equipment or number lines, together with
informal written methods such as drawing the 'jumps' on
the number lines, to find the answer to each of the
following questions by the process of taking away?

$12 - 5$	$21 - 3$	$14 - 8$
$23 - 9$	$32 - 4$	$41 - 7$

Administering the assessment

Provide the children with the Assessment sheet, which
shows a number line to 25 and ask them to complete the
questions. A variety of different counting equipment should
also be available, together with some number lines and
some blank sheets of paper so that the child can complete
informal jottings and number line drawings. Allow the
children plenty of time to complete the questions and
observe how they approach each one. Encourage the
children to explain to you what they are is doing. At this
stage there is not one 'correct' method. Providing each
child's method is logical, s/he can achieve Objective 1,
without having to use either the counting equipment or the
number lines. Note that this assessment is for the process
of 'taking away' rather than 'finding the difference' so pupils
should be physically 'taking away' or 'moving' counting
equipment so that they have less than their start number,
or they should be counting 'back' on a number line.

(Note that this assessment can be used to support your
assessment of Using and applying mathematics: Describe
simple patterns and relationships involving numbers or
shapes; decide whether examples satisfy given conditions;
Describe a puzzle or problem using numbers, practical
materials and diagrams; use these to solve the problem and
set the solution in the original context.)

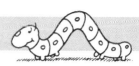

Understand subtraction as take away

Name

Date

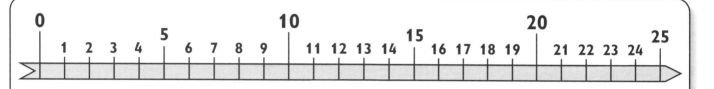

Number line: 0 1 2 3 4 5 6 7 8 9 10 11 12 13 14 15 16 17 18 19 20 21 22 23 24 25

Answer these questions:

$9 - 4 =$ ⬚

$7 - 3 =$ ⬚

$8 - 5 =$ ⬚

$6 - 1 =$ ⬚

$9 - 7 =$ ⬚

$5 - 0 =$ ⬚

Now try these questions:

$12 - 5 =$ ⬚

$21 - 3 =$ ⬚

$14 - 8 =$ ⬚

$23 - 9 =$ ⬚

$32 - 4 =$ ⬚

$41 - 7 =$ ⬚

I understand subtraction as 'take away'. ✏⬚

I can subtract a one-digit number from a one-digit number. ✏⬚

I can subtract a one-digit number from a two-digit number. ✏⬚

I can use equipment or written methods to help me. ✏⬚

Understand subtraction (of a multiple of 10) as take away

**Understand subtraction as take away
(use practical and informal written methods to
support the subtraction of a multiple of 10 from
a two-digit number)**

Building on previous learning

Before starting this unit check that the children can
already:

- count reliably at least 20 objects, recognising that when
  rearranged the number of objects stays the same.
- compare and order numbers, using the related
  vocabulary.
- read and write numerals from 0 to 20 then beyond; use
  knowledge of place value to position these numbers on a
  number track and number line.
- use the vocabulary related to subtraction and symbols
  to describe and record subtraction number sentences.
- count on or back in tens and derive the multiples of 10
  to the tenth multiple.

Learning objectives

Objective 1: Use practical and informal written methods
to support the subtraction of a multiple of 10 from a
two-digit number

Learning outcomes

The children will be able to:

- take away a multiple of 10 from a larger number.
- use practical equipment, such as counting apparatus in
  the form of counters, toys, etc.
- use number lines.

Success criteria

The children have a **secure** level of attainment in relation
to Objective 1 if the following questions can be answered
with a 'yes'.

Can the children…
… find the answers to the following questions, using a
  process of taking away?
  46 – 10   53 – 10   79 – 10?
… use counting equipment or number lines, together with
  informal written methods such as drawing the 'jumps' on
  the number lines, to find the answer to each of the
  following questions by the process of taking away?
  58 – 20   36 – 20   49 – 30   61 – 40
  28 – 20   99 – 70   16 – 10   81 – 50

Administering the assessment

Provide the children with the Assessment sheet, which
shows a number line to 100 and ask them to complete the
questions shown on the sheet. A variety of different
counting equipment should also be available, together with
some number lines and some blank sheets of paper so that
the child can complete informal jottings and number line
drawings. Allow the children plenty of time to complete the
questions and observe how they approach each one –
encourage them to explain to you what they are doing.

At this stage there is not a 'correct' method. Providing each
child's method is logical, to achieve the learning objective
s/he does not have to make use of both the counting
equipment and the number lines. Note that this assessment
is for the process of taking away rather than finding the
difference so pupils should be physically 'taking away' or
moving counting equipment so that they have less than
their start number, or they should be counting back on a
number line.

(Note that this assessment can be used to support your
assessment of Using and applying mathematics: Describe
simple patterns and relationships involving numbers or
shapes; decide whether examples satisfy given conditions;
Describe a puzzle or problem using numbers, practical
materials and diagrams; use these to solve the problem and
set the solution in the original context.)

Understand subtraction as take away

Name

Date

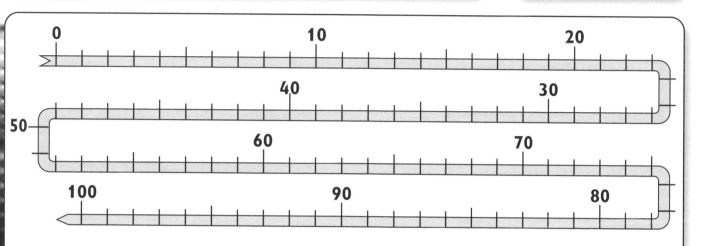

Answer these questions:

46 – 10 =

53 – 10 =

79 – 10 =

92 – 10 =

21 – 10 =

68 – 10 =

Now try these questions:

58 – 20 =

36 – 20 =

49 – 30 =

61 – 40 =

28 – 20 =

99 – 70 =

16 – 10 =

81 – 50 =

I understand subtraction as 'take away'.

I can subtract a multiple of 10 from a two-digit number.

I can use equipment or written methods to help me.

Understand subtraction as 'find the difference' by counting up

Understand subtraction as 'find the difference' by counting up (use practical and informal written methods to support the subtraction of a one-digit number from a one-digit or two-digit number and a multiple of 10 from a two-digit number)

Building on previous learning

Before starting this unit check that the children can already:

- count reliably at least 20 objects, recognising that when rearranged the number of objects stays the same
- compare and order numbers, using the related vocabulary
- read and write numerals from 0 to 20 then beyond; use knowledge of place value to position these numbers on a number track and number line
- use the vocabulary related to subtraction and symbols to describe and record subtraction number sentences
- count on or back in tens and derive the multiples of 10 to the tenth multiple.

Learning objectives

Objective 1: Use practical and informal written methods to support the subtraction of a one-digit number from a one-digit or two-digit number and a multiple of 10 from a two-digit number.

Learning outcomes

The children will be able to:
- find a difference by counting up to subtract a one-digit number from a one-digit or two-digit number or a multiple of 10 from a two-digit number.
- use practical equipment, such as counting apparatus in the form of counters, toys, etc.
- use number lines.

Success criteria

The children have a **secure** level of attainment in relation to Objective 1 if the following questions can be answered with a 'yes'.

Can the children...
... find the answers to the following questions, using a process of finding the difference by counting up:

9 – 7   14 – 9   13 – 8?

... use counting equipment or number lines, together with informal written methods such as drawing the 'jumps' on the number lines, to find the answer to each of the following questions by the process of finding the difference by counting up:

69 – 30	48 – 20	83 – 40	71 – 50
92 – 80	70 – 30	85 – 60	57 – 30?

Administering the assessment

Provide the children with Assessment sheet 24, which shows a number line to 100 and ask them to complete the questions shown on the sheet. A variety of different counting equipment should also be available, together with some number lines and some blank sheets of paper so that the child can complete informal jottings and number line drawings. Allow the children plenty of time to complete the questions and observe how they approach each one. Encourage them to explain to you what they are doing.

At this stage there is not a 'correct' method. Providing the child's method is logical, to achieve the learning objective s/he does not have to make use of both the counting equipment and the number lines. Note that this assessment is for the process of 'finding the difference' rather than 'taking away' so the children should be counting up from the smaller number to the larger number.

(Note that this assessment can be used to support your assessment of Using and applying mathematics: Describe simple patterns and relationships involving numbers or shapes; decide whether examples satisfy given conditions; Describe a puzzle or problem using numbers, practical materials and diagrams; use these to solve the problem and set the solution in the original context.)

Understand subtraction as 'find the difference' by counting up

Name

Date

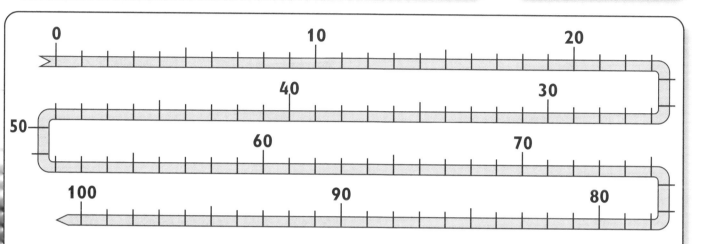

Answer these questions:

$9 - 7 =$ ⬚ $14 - 9 =$ ⬚ $13 - 8 =$ ⬚

Now try these questions:

$69 - 30 =$ ⬚ $48 - 20 =$ ⬚

$83 - 40 =$ ⬚ $71 - 50 =$ ⬚

$92 - 80 =$ ⬚ $70 - 30 =$ ⬚

$85 - 60 =$ ⬚ $57 - 30 =$ ⬚

I understand subtraction as finding a difference.

I can subtract a one-digit number from a one-digit or two-digit number.

I can subtract a multiple of 10 from a two-digit number. ✏️☐

I can use equipment or written methods to help me. ✏️☐

Andrew Brodie: Ten Minute Maths Assessments ages 5–6 © A&C Black 2009

Solve practical problems that involve combining groups of 2, 5 or 10

Building on previous learning

Before starting this unit check that the children can already:

- count reliably at least 20 objects, recognising that when rearranged the number of objects stays the same.
- compare and order numbers, using the related vocabulary.
- read and write numerals from 0 to 20 then beyond; use knowledge of place value to position these numbers on a number track and number line.
- count on in ones, twos, fives and tens.

Learning objectives

Objective 1: Solve practical problems that involve combining groups of 2, 5 or 10.

Learning outcomes

The children will be able to solve practical problems that involve:

- combining groups of 2.
- combining groups of 5.
- combining groups of 10.

Success criteria

The children have a **secure** level of attainment in relation to Objective 1 if the following questions can be answered with a 'yes'.

Can the children...

... find the total numbers of socks in specified numbers of pairs?
... find the total numbers of toes on specified numbers of feet?
... find the total numbers of pencils in specified numbers of pots of 10 pencils?

Administering the assessment

Use the opportunity to discuss practical situations involving socks, gloves, feet, toes, hands, fingers and pencils in pots of 10! It is essential that the children are provided with practical equipment to use when completing the assessment. Accordingly you will need to prepare 6 pairs of socks, some dolls with bare feet showing 5 toes each, and some pencils in pots of 10.

● Track 13 The CD can be used with the Assessment sheet and has the advantage of focussing pupils' attention on the task. This is the script for the CD if you decide to dictate the questions:

Look at question 1: There are 6 pairs of socks. How many socks are there altogether?
Question 2: If there are 3 pairs of socks, how many socks are there altogether?
Question 3: If there are 5 pairs of socks, how many socks are there altogether?
Now look at question 4: There are 5 feet. Each foot has 5 toes. How many toes are there altogether?
Question 5: If there are 2 feet, how many toes are there altogether?
Question 6: If there are 4 feet, how many toes are there altogether?
Look at question 7: Each pot has 10 pencils. There are 3 pots. How many pencils are there altogether?
You may decide to give extra questions relating to the pots of pencils.

(Note that this assessment can be used to support your assessment of Using and applying mathematics: Describe simple patterns and relationships involving numbers or shapes; decide whether examples satisfy given conditions; Describe a puzzle or problem using numbers, practical materials and diagrams; use these to solve the problem and set the solution in the original context; describe ways of solving puzzles or problems, explaining choices and decisions orally or using pictures.)

Solve practical problems that involve combining groups of 2, 5 or 10

Name

Date

1. There are 6 pairs of socks. How many socks are there altogether?

2.

3.

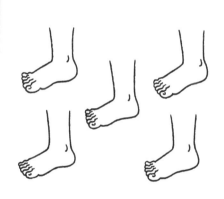

4. There are 5 feet. Each foot has 5 toes. How many toes are there altogether?

5.

6.

7. Each pot has 10 pencils. If there were 3 pots, how many pencils would there be altogether?

I can count on in twos to solve practical problems.

I can count on in fives to solve practical problems.

I can count on in 10s to solve practical problems.

Andrew Brodie: Ten Minute Maths Assessments ages 5–6 © A&C Black 2009

Solve practical problems that involve sharing into equal groups of 2, 5 or 10

Building on previous learning

Before starting this unit check that the children can already:

- count reliably at least 20 objects, recognising that when rearranged the number of objects stays the same.
- compare and order numbers, using the related vocabulary.
- read and write numerals from 0 to 20 then beyond; use knowledge of place value to position these numbers on a number track and number line.
- count on or back in ones, twos, fives and tens.
- share objects into equal groups and count how many in each group.

Learning objectives

Objective 1: Solve practical problems that involve sharing into equal groups of 2, 5 or 10.

Learning outcomes

The children will be able to solve practical problem that involve sharing:

- into groups of 2.
- into groups of 5.
- into groups of 10.

Success criteria

The children have a **secure** level of attainment in relation to Objective 1 if the following questions can be answered with a 'yes'.

Can the children...

... share counters to represent apples, into groups of 2?
... share counters to represent grapes, into groups of 5?
... share counters to represent strawberries, into groups of 10?

Administering the assessment

Use the opportunity to discuss practical situations involving various items of fruit. It is essential that the children are provided with practical equipment to use when completing the assessment. Accordingly you will need to prepare counters to represent the fruits featured on the sheet. The children may choose, instead, to draw pictures to help with their calculations and some space is allowed on the sheet but you may need to provide extra paper.

🔘 Track 14   The CD can be used with the Assessment sheet and has the advantage of focussing pupils' attention on the task. This is the script for the CD if you decide to dictate the questions:

Look at question 1: There are 8 apples. How many children could have 2 apples each?
Now look at question 2: There are 20 grapes. How many children could have 5 grapes each?
Now look at question 3: There are 30 strawberries. How many children could have 10 strawberries each?

You may wish to gain further evidence by asking more questions:
If there are 6 apples, how many children could have 2 apples each?
If there are 15 grapes, how many children could have 5 grapes each?
If there are 50 strawberries, how many children could have 10 strawberries each?

(Note that this assessment can be used to support your assessment of Using and applying mathematics: Describe simple patterns and relationships involving numbers or shapes; decide whether examples satisfy given conditions; Describe a puzzle or problem using numbers, practical materials and diagrams; use these to solve the problem and set the solution in the original context; describe ways of solving puzzles or problems, explaining choices and decisions orally or using pictures.)

Solve practical problems that involve sharing into equal groups

Name

Date

1. There are 8 apples.
   How many children could have
   2 apples each?

   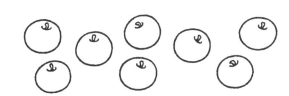

2. There are 20 grapes.
   How many children could have
   5 grapes each?

   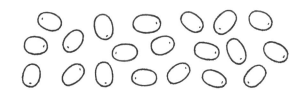

3. There are 30 strawberries.
   How many children could have
   10 strawberries each?

I can share in twos to solve practical problems.

I can share in fives to solve practical problems.

I can share in tens to solve practical problems.

Visualise and name common 2-D shapes and describe their features

Building on previous learning

Before starting this unit check that the children can already:
- use familiar objects and common shapes to create and recreate patterns and build models.
- use language such as 'circle' or 'bigger' to describe the shape and size of solids and flat shapes.
- use everyday words to describe position.

Learning objectives

Objective 1: Visualise and name common 2-D shapes and describe their features.

Learning outcomes

The children will be able to:
- name the following shapes: circle, triangle, square, rectangle.
- describe the features of each of the shapes.

Success criteria

The children have a **secure** level of attainment in relation to Objective 1 if the following questions can be answered with a 'yes'.

Can the children...
... identify each of the shapes shown on the Assessment sheet?
... describe the number of sides of the triangle, square, rectangle?
... describe the number of corners of the triangle, square, rectangle?
... explain that the circle has only one side and no corners?
... explain that the circle has a curved side and the other shapes have straight sides?

Administering the assessment

Provide the children with the Assessment sheet, which shows a circle, triangle, square and rectangle. Discuss each shape with the children, asking the following questions:

Do you know what this shape is? How many sides has it got? How many corners has it got?

You could extend the exercise by asking the following questions:

Which shape do you think is the odd one out?
Which 2 shapes have the same number of sides?
Which 2 shapes have the same number of corners?
Which shape has 3 sides and 3 corners?

You could supply the children with some prepared shapes that they can use to make patterns, pictures and models. Encourage them to talk about the shapes as they use them.

(Note that this assessment can be used to support your assessment of Using and applying mathematics: Describe simple patterns and relationships involving numbers or shapes; decide whether examples satisfy given conditions; Answer a question by selecting and using suitable equipment, and sorting information, shapes or objects; display results using tables and pictures.)

Visualise and name common 2-D shapes and describe their features

59

Name

Date

Talk about the shapes.

I can name common 2-D shapes. ✏️ ☐

I can describe the features of 2-D shapes. ✏️ ☐

Visualise and name common 3-D solids and describe their features

Building on previous learning

Before starting this unit check that the children can already:
- use familiar objects and common shapes to create and recreate patterns and build models.
- use language such as 'circle' or 'bigger' to describe the shape and size of solids and flat shapes.
- use everyday words to describe position.

Learning objectives

Objective 1: Visualise and name common 3-D solids and describe their features.

Learning outcomes

The children will be able to:
- name the following solids: cube, cuboid, pyramid, sphere, cone, cylinder.
- describe the features of each of the solids.

Success criteria

The children have a **secure** level of attainment in relation to Objective 1 if the following questions can be answered with a 'yes'.

Can the children...
... identify each of the solids shown on the Assessment sheet?
... describe the number of faces of each solid?
... describe the number of points of each solid, apart from the cylinder and sphere?
... describe the number of edges of each solid, apart from the sphere?
... explain that the sphere has only one face and no edges or points?
... explain that the cone and the cylinder have curved faces and flat faces; the sphere has a curved face; and the other solids have only flat faces?

Administering the assessment

Provide the children with the Assessment sheet, which shows drawings of a cube, cuboid, pyramid, sphere, cone and cylinder. It is essential that the children are supplied with actual 3-D solids and do not base their descriptions on the illustrations. Discuss each solid with the children, asking the following questions:

Do you know what this solid is called? How many faces has it got? How many points has it got? How many edges has it got?

You could extend the exercise by asking the following questions:

Which 2 solids have the same number of faces?
Which 2 solids have the same number of points?
Which 2 solids have no points?

You could supply the children with some prepared solids that they can use to make models. Encourage them to talk about the solids as they use them.

(Note that this assessment can be used to support your assessment of Using and applying mathematics: Describe simple patterns and relationships involving numbers or shapes; decide whether examples satisfy given conditions; Answer a question by selecting and using suitable equipment, and sorting information, shapes or objects; display results using tables and pictures.)

Visualise and name common 3-D solids and describe their features

Name

Date

Here are some pictures of solid shapes.

Hold each solid shape in your hands.

Talk about each solid shape.

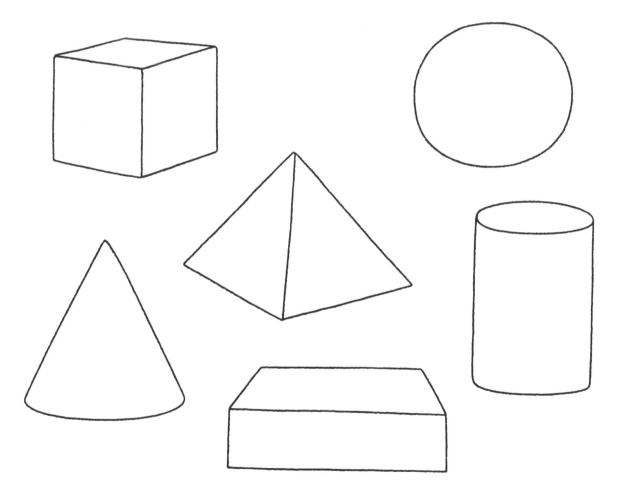

I can name common 3-D solids.

I can describe the features of 3-D solids.

Andrew Brodie: Ten Minute Maths Assessments ages 5–6 © A&C Black 2009

Identify objects that turn about a point or about a line

Identify objects that turn about a point or about a line (recognise and make whole, half and quarter turns)

Building on previous learning

Before starting this unit check that the children can already:
- use everyday words to describe position.
- use the vocabulary of halves and quarters in context.

Learning objectives

Objective 1: Identify objects that turn about a point or about a line.
Objective 2: Recognise and make whole, half and quarter turns.

Learning outcomes

The children will be able to:
- identify objects that turn about a point, such as scissors, clock hands.
- identify objects that turn about a line, such as doors, hinged lids.
- recognise and make whole, half and quarter turns.

Success criteria

The children have a **secure** level of attainment in relation to Objective 1 if the following questions can be answered with a 'yes'.

Can the children...
... identify the line about which a door turns or the line about which a hinged lid turns?
... identify the point about which a pair of scissors turns or the point about which the clock hands turn?

The children have a **secure** level of attainment in relation to Objective 2 if the following questions can be answered with a 'yes'.

Can the children...
... demonstrate a whole turn of the 'hand' on the rotation disk made from the template on the Assessment sheet?
... demonstrate a half turn of the 'hand' on the rotation disk?
... demonstrate a quarter turn of the 'hand' on the rotation disk?

Administering the assessment

Observe the movement of doors and hinged lids with the children, encouraging them to identify the line about which each rotates. Now look at a pair of scissors and a clock face, encouraging the children to identify the point of rotation.

Photocopy the Assessment sheet on to thin card. Help the children to cut out the disk and the 'hand', then to fasten the hand to the disk with a paper joiner to create a rotation disk. Ask the children to demonstrate a whole turn, a half turn and a quarter turn.

(Note that this assessment can be used to support your assessment of Using and applying mathematics: Describe simple patterns and relationships involving numbers or shapes; decide whether examples satisfy given conditions; Answer a question by selecting and using suitable equipment, and sorting information, shapes or objects; display results using tables and pictures.)

Identify objects that turn about a point or about a line

Name

Date

Cut out the circle to make a disk.

Cut out the hand.

Fasten the hand to the disk.

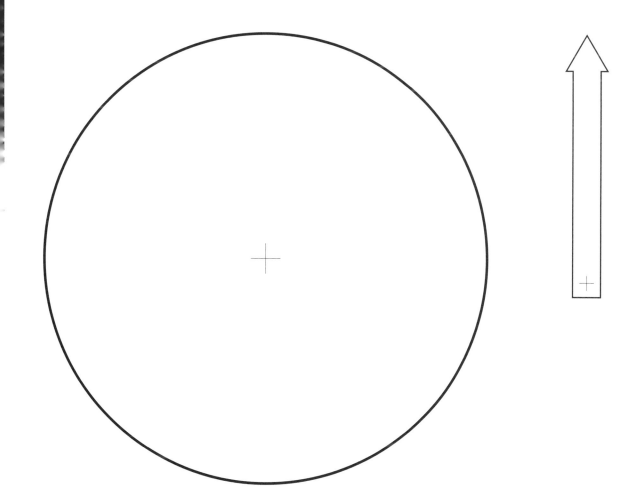

I can identify lines of rotation and points of rotation.

I can recognise and make whole, half and quarter turns.

Use vocabulary related to time (Order days of the week)

Building on previous learning

Before starting this unit check that the children can already:

- use everyday language related to time; order and sequence familiar events and measure short periods of time.

Learning objectives

Objective 1: Use vocabulary related to time.
Objective 2: Order days of the week.

Learning outcomes

The children will be able to:

- use vocabulary related to time.
- say the names of the days of the week in order.
- write or stick the names of the days of the week in order.

Success criteria

The children have a **secure** level of attainment in relation to Objective 1 if the following questions can be answered with a 'yes'.

Can the children...

... talk about events using vocabulary such as: day, week, month, year, spring, summer, autumn, winter, weekend, birthday, holiday, morning, afternoon, evening, night, midnight, today, yesterday, tomorrow, before, after, next, last, now, soon, early, late, fast, slow, old, new, how long ago? How long will it be to...? How long will it take to ...? How often? always, often, sometimes, usually?

The children have a **secure** level of attainment in relation to Objective 2 if the following question can be answered with a 'yes'.

Can the children...

... sort the days of the week into the correct order?

Administering the assessment

The first part of the assessment should be conducted orally by an adult working with a small group of children. Encourage the children to talk about issues related to time, such as days of the week, birthdays, months, seasons, e.g. you could ask what day it is today then lead the children to discuss yesterday, tomorrow, the month, the year, etc. If possible allow the children to direct the discussion themselves, steering them back to time issues every time they wander!

For the second part of the assessment photocopy the Assessment sheet on to thin card. Help the children to cut out the names of the days of the week, which are presented in random order. Their task is to arrange the days in order. They could stick the words on to a separate piece of paper or copy them down. Note, however, that if they are not able to read or write the words they will still achieve the learning objective if they can name the days in order orally.

Use vocabulary related to time (Order days of the week)

Name

Date

Saturday

Wednesday

Monday

Thursday

Sunday

Tuesday

Friday

I know lots of words about time.

I can say the days of the week in order.

Andrew Brodie: Ten Minute Maths Assessments ages 5–6 © A&C Black 2009

Use vocabulary related to time (Order months of the year)

Building on previous learning

Before starting this unit check that the children can already:
- use everyday language related to time; order and sequence familiar events and measure short periods of time.

Learning objectives

Objective 1: Use vocabulary related to time.
Objective 2: Order months of the year.

Learning outcomes

The children will be able to:
- use vocabulary related to time.
- say the names of the months of the year in order.
- write or stick the names of the months of the year in order.

Success criteria

The children have a **secure** level of attainment in relation to Objective 1 if the following questions can be answered with a 'yes'.

Can the children…
… talk about events using vocabulary such as: day, week, month, year, spring, summer, autumn, winter, weekend, birthday, holiday, morning, afternoon, evening, night, midnight, today, yesterday, tomorrow, before, after, next, last, now, soon, early, late, fast, slow, old, new. How long ago? How long will it be to …? How long will it take to …? How often? always, often, sometimes, usually?

The children have a **secure** level of attainment in relation to Objective 2 if the following questions can be answered with a 'yes'.

Can the children…
… sort the months of the year into the correct order?

Administering the assessment

The first part of the assessment should be conducted orally by an adult working with a small group of children. As in the last assessment, encourage the children to talk about time this time with a historical perspective e.g. you could ask the children how long ago they think the school was built, how old do they think the school is, how old are they? Their answers to these questions do not need to be accurate as time is an extremely difficult concept. However, what is being assessed is their use of language so you will need to make a judgement as to how well each child is able to discuss concepts of time.

For the second part of the assessment photocopy the Assessment sheet on to thin card. Help the children to cut out the names of the months of the year, which are presented in random order. Their task is to arrange the months in order. They could stick the words on to a separate piece of paper or copy them down. Note, however, that if they are not able to read or write the words they will still achieve the learning objective if they can name the months in order orally. This is a very demanding task!

Use vocabulary related to time (Order months of the year)

Name

Date

September	March
August	May
December	January
April	October
July	February
November	June

I know lots of words about time.

I can say the months of the year in order.

Andrew Brodie: Ten Minute Maths Assessments ages 5–6 © A&C Black 2009

Read the time to the hour

Building on previous learning

Before starting this unit check that the children can already:

- use everyday language related to time; order and sequence familiar events and measure short periods of time.

Learning objectives

Objective 1: Read the time to the hour.

Learning outcomes

The children will be able to:

- use vocabulary related to time.
- read the time to the hour.

Success criteria

The children have a **secure** level of attainment in relation to Objective 1 if the following question can be answered with a 'yes'.

Can the children...

... identify the times shown on the clock faces on the Assessment sheet?

Administering the assessment

Ask the children to look carefully at each clock face and to tell you the time shown or to write the appropriate time on the Assessment sheet. Note, however, that if the children are not able to read or write the words they will still achieve the learning objective if they can say the times orally.

● **Track 15** As an extension activity you could use the Assessment sheet on page 80. This Assessment sheet shows blank clock faces and the children can enter times by drawing hands as instructed on the CD track. This is the script for the CD if you decide to dictate the questions:

Find clock A: Draw hands on the clock to show the time 7 o'clock.
Find clock B: Draw hands on the clock to show the time 10 o'clock.
Find clock C: Draw hands on the clock to show the time 2 o'clock.
Find clock D: Draw hands on the clock to show the time 5 o'clock.
Find clock E: Draw hands on the clock to show the time 6 o'clock.
Find clock F: Draw hands on the clock to show the time 9 o'clock.

Andrew Brodie: Ten Minute Maths Assessments ages 5–6 © A&C Black 200

Read the time to the hour

Name

Date

Listen carefully to the CD or your teacher.

3 o'clock

I can read the time to the hour.

Andrew Brodie: Ten Minute Maths Assessments ages 5–6 © A&C Black 2009

Read the time to the half-hour

Building on previous learning

Before starting this unit check that the children can already:

- use everyday language related to time; order and sequence familiar events and measure short periods of time

Learning objectives

Objective 1: Read the time to the half hour.

Learning outcomes

The children will be able to:

- use vocabulary related to time.
- read the time to the half hour.

Success criteria

The children have a **secure** level of attainment in relation to Objective 1 if the following questions can be answered with a 'yes'.

Can the children...

... identify the times shown on the clock faces on the Assessment sheet?

Administering the assessment

Ask the child to look carefully at each clock face and to tell you the time shown or to write the appropriate time on the Assessment sheet. Note, however, that if the child is not able to read or write the words they will still achieve the learning objective if they can say the times orally.

Track 16 As an extension activity you could use the Assessment sheet on page 80. This sheet shows blank clock faces and the children can enter times by drawing hands as instructed on the CD track. This is the script for the CD if you decide to dictate the questions:

Find clock A: Draw hands on the clock to show the time half past 8.
Find clock B: Draw hands on the clock to show the time half past 1.
Find clock C: Draw hands on the clock to show the time half past 4.
Find clock D: Draw hands on the clock to show the time half past 6.
Find clock E: Draw hands on the clock to show the time half past 3.
Find clock F: Draw hands on the clock to show the time half past 9.

Read the time to the half-hour

Name

Date

Listen carefully to the CD or your teacher.

half past 4

I can read the time to the half hour.

Andrew Brodie: Ten Minute Maths Assessments ages 5–6 © A&C Black 2009

Answer a question by recording information in lists and tables

Building on previous learning

Before starting this unit check that the children can already:

- sort familiar objects to identify their similarities and differences.
- count how many objects share a particular property, presenting results using pictures, drawings or numerals.

Learning objectives

Objective 1: Answer a question by recording information in lists and tables.

Learning outcomes

The children will be able to:

- sort a list of items of food and drink into a simple table.

Success criteria

The children have a **secure** level of attainment in relation to Objective 1 if the following question can be answered with a 'yes'.

Can the children…

… sort the items on the Assessment sheet into a list of foods and drinks?

Administering the assessment

Help the children to read the words that are shown with the illustrations. Discuss the food and drink items, accepting the fact that drinks are also food items if a child raises this but pointing out that this exercise is about sorting the items into those that we drink and those that we eat.

🔘 Track 17   You may wish to use the audio track from the CD or you may prefer to dictate it to the child – in either case pause after each question to allow the child to give an oral answer. The text is as follows:

Look carefully at the pictures.
Can you find the milk? Do you drink milk or eat milk?
Can you find the bread? Do you drink bread or eat bread?
Can you find the water? Do you drink water or eat water?
Can you find the apple? Do you drink an apple or eat an apple?
Can you find the orange juice? Do you drink orange juice or eat orange juice?
Can you find the banana? Do you drink a banana or eat a banana?
Can you find the chocolate? Do you drink chocolate or eat chocolate?
On a separate sheet of paper draw a table to show a list of things we eat and a list of things we drink.

The children can draw the table then write the names of items in each list or cut out and stick the pictures of the items on the sheet in the appropriate columns. The children may need your help in writing titles for the columns on the table but the table itself should be their own design.

(Note that this assessment can be used to support your assessment of Using and applying mathematics: Answer a question by selecting and using suitable equipment, and sorting information, shapes or objects; display results using tables and pictures.)

Andrew Brodie: Ten Minute Maths Assessments ages 5–6 © A&C Black 2009

Answer a question by recording information in lists and tables

Name

Date

Listen carefully to the CD or your teacher.

milk

apple

orange juice

banana

bread

chocolate

water

I can record information in lists and tables.

Present outcomes using practical resources, pictures, block graphs or pictograms

Building on previous learning

Before starting this unit check that the children can already:

- sort familiar objects to identify their similarities and differences.
- count how many objects share a particular property, presenting results using pictures, drawings or numerals.

Learning objectives

Objective 1: Present outcomes using practical resources, pictures, block graphs or pictograms.

Learning outcomes

The children will be able to:

- create a pictogram showing favourite fruits.

Success criteria

The children have a **secure** level of attainment in relation to Objective 1 if the following question can be answered with a 'yes'.

Can the children...

... use the picture of fruit on the Assessment sheet to create a pictogram showing the favourite fruits of children in the class?

Administering the assessment

This assessment can be carried out by several children at the same time.

Help each child to cut out the pictures of fruit shown on the sheet and to create a simple grid for a pictogram. Conduct a survey in the class by asking children to choose a favourite fruit from those shown. The children will need to record the results by sticking each child's chosen fruit into the appropriate column. You may wish to extend the activity by using the information from the pictogram to create a block graph.

(Note that this assessment can be used to support your assessment of Using and applying mathematics: Answer a question by selecting and using suitable equipment, and sorting information, shapes or objects; display results using tables and pictures.)

Andrew Brodie: Ten Minute Maths Assessments ages 5–6 © A&C Black 2009

Present outcomes using practical resources, pictures, block graphs or pictograms

Name

Date

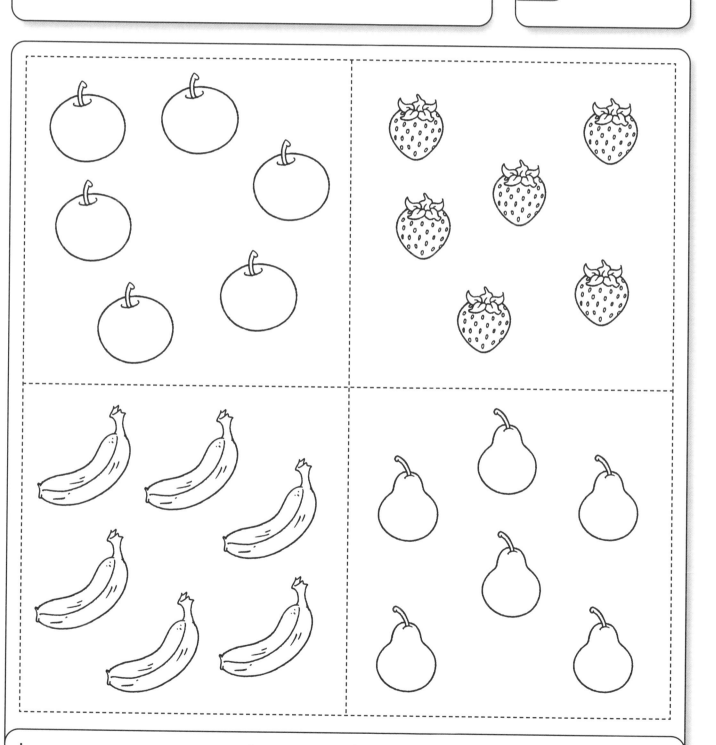

I can present outcomes using practical resources, pictures, block graphs or pictograms.

Andrew Brodie: Ten Minute Maths Assessments ages 5–6 © A&C Black 2009

Use diagrams to sort objects into groups according to a given criterion

Use diagrams to sort objects into groups according to a given criterion (suggest a different criterion for grouping the same objects)

Building on previous learning

Before starting this unit check that the children can already:
- sort familiar objects to identify their similarities and differences.
- count how many objects share a particular property, presenting results using pictures, drawings or numerals.

Learning objectives

Objective 1: Use diagrams to sort objects into groups according to a given criterion.

Objective 2: Suggest a different criterion for grouping the same objects .

Learning outcomes

The children will be able to:
- sort pictures of squares and circles into sorting hoops.
- sort the same pictures in a different way, ie into big and small shapes.

Success criteria

The children have a **secure** level of attainment in relation to Objective 1 if the following question can be answered with a 'yes'.

Can the children...
... sort the pictures according to the attribute of shape, quickly and effectively?

The children have a **secure** level of attainment in relation to Objective 2 if the following question can be answered with a 'yes'.

Can the children...
... find an alternative way of sorting the pictures e.g. by size?

Administering the assessment

Help the children to cut out the pictures of squares and circles. Prepare some sorting hoops and ask the children to sort the pictures into the hoops according to whether they are squares or circles. Now ask the children to remove the pictures from the circles and ask them if they can think of an alternative way to sort them. The obvious way to sort them is according to size i.e. large and small. However, this will not necessarily be obvious to the children.

(Note that this assessment can be used to support your assessment of Using and applying mathematics: Describe simple patterns and relationships involving numbers or shapes; decide whether examples satisfy given conditions; Answer a question by selecting and using suitable equipment, and sorting information, shapes or objects; display results using tables or pictures.)

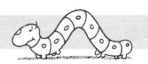

Use diagrams to sort objects into groups according to a given criterion

Name

Date

I can sort objects into groups according to given criterion.

I can suggest a different way of sorting the objects.

Andrew Brodie: Ten Minute Maths Assessments ages 5–6 © A&C Black 2009

Solving problems involving adding and subtracting in the context of money

Building on previous learning

Before starting this unit check that the children can already:

- derive and recall all pairs of numbers with a total of 10.
- derive and recall addition facts for totals to at least 5.
- work out the corresponding subtraction facts.
- count on or back in ones, twos, fives and tens.
- relate addition to counting on.
- understand subtraction as take away and find a difference by counting up.
- use the vocabulary related to addition and subtraction and symbols to describe and record addition and subtraction number sentences.
- use the equals sign.

Learning objectives

Objective 1: Solving problems involving adding in the context of money.

Objective 2: Solving problems involving subtracting in the context of money.

Learning outcomes

The children will be able to:

- find total amounts to pay for 2 items.
- find change when buying an item.

Success criteria

The children have a **secure** level of attainment in relation to Objective 1 if the following question can be answered with a 'yes'.

Can the children…
… add together 2 sums of money in pence to find the total cost of 2 priced items?

The children have a **secure** level of attainment in relation to Objective 2 if the following question can be answered with a 'yes'.

Can the children…
… find the change from 10 pence or 20 pence when buying some priced items?

Administering the assessment

Track 18 Ensure that there are some coins available for the children to use if they wish. Discuss the pictures with the children, establishing the context of a fete or a car boot sale. Now play the CD, ensuring that the children understand where to write the answers. You will need to pause the CD after each question to give the children time to work out the answers. This is the script for the CD if you decide to dictate the questions.

If I buy the teddy and the ball, what is the total cost?
If I buy the toy car and the pencil, what is the total cost?
If I buy the toy car and the ball, what is the total cost?
If I buy the teddy and the pencil, what is the total cost?
I have 10 pence to spend. If I buy the teddy how much change will I have?
I have 10 pence to spend. If I buy the ball how much change will I have?
I now have 20 pence to spend. If I buy the teddy how much change will I have?
I now have 20 pence to spend. If I buy the pencil how much change will I have?

(Note that this assessment can be used to support your assessment of Using and applying mathematics: Solve problems involving counting, adding, subtracting, doubling or halving in the context of numbers, measures or money, for example to pay or give change; Answer a question by selecting and using suitable equipment, and sorting information, shapes or objects; display results using tables and pictures; Describe ways of solving puzzles and problems, explaining choices and decisions orally or using pictures.)

Solving problems involving adding and subtracting in the context of money

Name

Date

If I buy the teddy and the ball, what is the total cost?

If I buy the toy car and the pencil, what is the total cost?

If I buy the toy car and the ball, what is the total cost?

If I buy the teddy and the pencil, what is the total cost?

I have 10 pence to spend.
If I buy the teddy how much change will I have?

I have 10 pence to spend.
If I buy the ball how much change will I have?

I now have 20 pence to spend.
If I buy the teddy how much change will I have?

I now have 20 pence to spend.
If I buy the pencil how much change will I have?

I can solve problems involving adding in the context of money.

I can solve problems involving subtracting in the context of money.

Supplementary sheet for use with Assessments 32 and 33

A

B

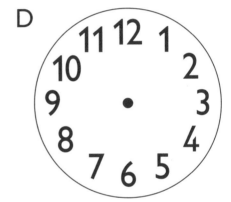

C

D

E

F

G

H

Andrew Brodie: Ten Minute Maths Assessments ages 5–6 © A&C Black 2009